United States Bureau of Engraving and Printing

Main Building — 1914 to the Present

A GUIDE BOOK

of

MODERN UNITED STATES CURRENCY

By
NEIL SHAFER

With Special Assistance From
WILLIAM P. DONLON

A Comprehensive Illustrated Valuation
Catalog of All Modern-Size United States
Paper Money From 1929 to the Present,
With Historical Information and Official
Bureau of Engraving Totals for Each Issue.

WHITMAN PUBLISHING COMPANY
RACINE, WISCONSIN

TABLE OF CONTENTS

TABLE OF CONTENTS (*Continued*)

Preface

A rather recent numismatic phenomenon has been the development of a strong interest in collecting modern U.S. currency. There have been many variations in type and series since the current-size notes were introduced to circulation on July 10, 1929, but only in the past year or two have collectors been actively seeking the different pieces.

Perhaps the one big push came in November of 1963 when Federal Reserve $1 notes with identifying marks from each of the twelve Federal Reserve Banks were released. Many collectors then began to realize for the first time that some varieties of the "ever-present" Silver Certificates might soon be scarce. Half-forgotten facts concerning the addition of the motto to various notes suddenly became compellingly important, and the hunt was on.

There has been comparatively little information published on these notes until recently. Robert Friedberg incorporated a listing of them in his well-known catalog. In October of 1964, William P. Donlon made a tremendous contribution to the study of modern U.S. currency with his book which contains much of the same information as that in the present volume. Both make extensive use of the compilation of records recently prepared by the Bureau of Engraving, which gave data never before available on totals printed and dates of delivery. The Donlon Simplified Numbering System is also incorporated here, since it is felt his system is especially well suited to the peculiarities of modern notes.

All available source material was thoroughly researched to provide the comprehensive and highly important supplementary data contained in this book. Included are such features as a diagram describing basic nomenclature, and careful explanations of popularly known terms. It is sincerely hoped that, armed with this information, the collector entering this field can successfully meet the great challenge offered in the study and acquisition of modern U.S. currency.

ACKNOWLEDGEMENTS

Appreciation and sincere thanks are extended to the following who have contributed suggestions, valuations and information to add to the completeness of this work:

Thomas C. Bain
A. E. Bebee
Lawrence Block
Kenneth E. Bressett
John McKnight Brown
Nathan Goldstein II
M. L. Kaplan
Theodore Kemm

A. Kosoft
Robert H. Lloyd
Lester Merkin
W. A. Philpott, Jr.
Thomas B. Ross
Dr. Kenneth J. Sartoris
G. A. Siegwart
Louis Werner

The Bureau of Engraving and Printing for invaluable assistance, and to Mrs. Catherine B. Andreasen, Edward Metzger, Jr. and Mrs. Eve M. Jubanyik for countless hours of research and compilation.

Mr. William P. Donlon, well-known authority and specialist in U. S. currency and author of his own book on the subject, gave tirelessly of his talents in checking over the Bureau compilation as well as supervising and preparing the valuations found in the catalog. To him goes a special word of thanks.

ILLUSTRATIONS

Notes for illustration are from the Donlon Reference Collection. The art work on page 8 is by Mr. Robert B. Kissner.

GLOSSARY OF CURRENCY TERMS

The following diagram illustrates the respective positions of the many characters and symbols found on modern U. S. currency issues. The nomenclature will be fully explained in succeeding sections of the book.

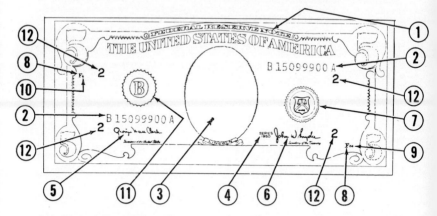

*1. TYPE OF NOTE — Federal Reserve Note, Silver Certificate, United States Note, National Currency.

2. SERIAL NUMBER — Every note has two identical serial numbers.

3. PORTRAIT — Each denomination carries a distinctive portrait.

4. SERIES DATE — The indicated position is for notes of later issue. Earlier printings carry the series date two times on the face, and in varying positions.

5. SIGNATURE — Treasurer of the United States.

6. SIGNATURE — Secretary of the Treasury.

7. TREASURY SEAL — Blue, green, red, brown, gold or yellow.

8. CHECK LETTERS — Each note has two identical check letters which indicate its sheet position.

9. FACE PLATE NUMBER — Found with the lower right Check Letter on all notes.

10. QUADRANT NUMBER — Going from 1 to 4, this is found only on issues printed in sheets of 32 notes.

11. FEDERAL RESERVE BANK SEAL — Found only on Federal Reserve Notes.

12. FEDERAL RESERVE DISTRICT NUMBERS — Found only on Federal Reserve Notes.

*Gold Certificates do not have the Type Heading in the usual position at the top.

BRIEF HISTORY OF THE
BUREAU OF ENGRAVING AND PRINTING

(Based on a Bureau publication of the same title)

Organization and Growth

The Bureau of Engraving and Printing was created out of necessity rather than law, since there was no organic act which authorized its establishment nor any legislation providing for the appointment of its officers. It was really not needed prior to 1861, as no federal paper money had been issued up to that time. However, the outbreak of the Civil War in 1861 forced the government to introduce paper money as a substitute for coins which had practically disappeared from circulation. The first issue was authorized by Acts of Congress of July 17 and August 5, 1861, and February 12, 1862, which required the Secretary of the Treasury to issue Demand Notes signed by the Treasurer of the United States, the Register of the Treasury, and other officials whom he might designate. These Demand Notes were printed by private bank note companies for the Treasury Department.

The Bureau came into functional existence because of an Act of Congress of July 11, 1862. A new issue of currency was authorized by that Act, and the Secretary of the Treasury was empowered to have some or all the notes engraved and printed by private firms or at the Treasury Department, and to prepare them for circulation by providing the necessary machinery, materials and personnel to accomplish this task. Operations commenced on August 29, 1862, when a force of two men and four women working in a single room in the attic of the main Treasury building began to separate, seal, and sign $1 and $2 notes which had been printed by private contractors. In November 1862, the First Division of the National Currency Bureau, later called the Bureau of Engraving and Printing, also commenced the printing of currency notes from plates engraved by Treasury employees. By 1864, it had become apparent that the United States government was to be indefinitely engaged in the manufacture of paper money. It was therefore recommended to the Secretary of the Treasury that "The Engraving and Printing Bureau of the Treasury Department" be established; however, the proposal was not accepted at that time. Congressional legislation finally recognized its existence in the Appropriation Act of August 15, 1876, and it has since functioned as a distinct entity within the Treasury Department.

As the years progressed, the Bureau of Engraving and Printing gradually absorbed the functions performed by the private bank note companies, and by October 1, 1877, the printing of all United States securities was centralized in the Bureau. The printing of internal revenue stamps was taken over in 1876 and the production of postage stamps in 1894.

From 1862 until 1880, all Bureau functions were housed in the main Treasury building. In 1880, Congress appropriated $300,000 for the purchase of a site and erection of a separate building for the Bureau. This is the red brick edifice which stands today just north of the present main building. By 1914, the Bureau operations had increased to such an extent that a larger building was needed. In the spring of that year, the Bureau occupied the present main building which had just been completed at a cost of approximately $3,000,000. The Bureau Annex, directly across from the main building, was completed in 1938. Thus, in a little over a century the Bureau has grown from a small unit of six persons to a large modern factory housed in two buildings with a combined floor space of close to 30 acres, and employing about 3,400 people.

Products of the Bureau

The Bureau in many ways resembles a private contracting firm. It receives orders for work from almost every branch of the government. But the greatest number of orders are received from four agencies — the Treasury Department, Federal Reserve System, Internal Revenue Service, and Post Office Department. The Bureau performs the work contracted for and is reimbursed for all work delivered.

The Bureau designs, engraves, and prints currency, bonds, Treasury notes and bills, postage and revenue stamps, checks and miscellaneous engraved work for the various governmental departments and independent establishments, and the insular possessions. Printings cover a wide range of subject matter from the ½¢ postage stamps to the lofty $500,000,000 Treasury note, officers' commissions printed on artificial parchment, invitations and admission cards to White House receptions, diplomas for the Coast Guard Academy, and certificates of meritorious awards made to service personnel by the Army and Navy. In addition to work printed from engraved plates, numerous items are produced on surface printing presses from offset plates. Such work includes liquor stamps and United States savings bonds ($500, $1,000, $5,000, and $10,000 in Series H; $25, $100, $500, $1,000, $5,000, $10,000, and $100,000 in Series J; $25, $50, $100, $200, $500, and $1,000 in Series E, 1943 design, and the new Kennedy $75 Series E issued in 1964).

The $75 Kennedy Savings Bond

The principal product of the Bureau is paper currency. Regardless of the type of bill issued, all those of like denomination bear the same portrait, and the backs are of uniform design. There are twelve denominations of currency ranging from $1 to $100,000. However, the $100,000 note is a Gold Certificate issued only to the Federal Reserve Banks; it never entered into public circulation. The $100 note is the highest denomination printed since 1945.

Designing and Preparations for Printing

When a new item is to be produced, a model is prepared by a designer after discussions with officials of agencies interested in the product. By tradition, portraits used for securities and regular issue stamps are those of Americans of historical importance. Portraits used on currency are of persons whose places in the annals of our country are particularly well known to the public.

TABLE OF PORTRAITS AND DESIGNS

Denomination	Portrait on Face	Design on Back
$1	George Washington	Great Seal
$2	Thomas Jefferson	Monticello
$5	Abraham Lincoln	Lincoln Memorial
$10	Alexander Hamilton	U. S. Treasury
$20	Andrew Jackson	White House
$50	Ulysses S. Grant	U. S. Capitol
$100	Benjamin Franklin	Independence Hall
$500	William McKinley	Value
$1000	Grover Cleveland	Value
$5000	James Madison	Value
$10,000	Salmon P. Chase	Value
$100,000	Woodrow Wilson	Value

The separate features of a given design are hand-tooled by engravers who cut v-shaped incised lines in soft pieces of steel. The separate engravings, called dies, are hardened and then transferred onto a cylindrical roll to form one composite design. The engraving is then known as the master roll. Without loss of distinctive detail this master engraving is transferred through various processes until it reaches the press as a multiple plate ready for production. Each feature, such as the portrait, lettering, scrollwork, and the lacy geometric patterns, is executed by an artist skilled in a particular field.

Papers and Inks

To guard against counterfeiting, United States paper money is printed by engraved intaglio (incuse design) steel plates on distinctive paper. The currency paper for dry printing is made of 75% cotton and 25% linen. For wet printing, the fiber content of the currency paper is 50% cotton and 50% linen. Both types contain small segments of red and blue fibers which are imbedded during manufacture. Strict government control is exercised during the preparation of this distinctive paper.

For the past 85 years, the firm of Crane and Company, Dalton, Massachusetts, was the sole producer of currency paper for the Bureau. In 1964, the Meade Paper Corporation of Dayton, Ohio, became a second source of this paper as its subsidiary firm, Gilbert Paper Company, Menasha, Wisconsin, prepared two shipments for the Bureau during that year.

Every sheet of paper requisitioned for printing must be accounted for. Sheets or notes found to be defective are canceled and sent to an audit unit for verification and delivery to the Destruction Committee. This Committee, under the jurisdiction of the U. S. Treasurer, arranges for final disposition. Through a system of internal checks, the Bureau is able to maintain strict accountability over each operating section. As a further safeguard, currency paper (for 18-subject sheets) is counted 12 times from its receipt as blank sheets to its delivery as finished notes.

All inks used in plate and surface printing are manufactured in the Bureau by blending dry colors, oils and extenders of the highest quality obtainable in huge mixers similar to the large kneading machines used by commercial bakeries. The blended ink mixtures are ground under extreme pressure in large mills between water-cooled heavy steel rollers to ensure the proper texture. A test is made of each new batch to see that it conforms with laboratory standards before it is used for printing.

The amount of paper and ink used by the Bureau for a single fiscal year is enormous. As an example, for Fiscal Year 1962, approximately 4,259 tons of paper and 1,162 tons of ink were used for the Bureau's production.

Wet Printing

The so-called "wet process" has been the chief method of currency production by the Bureau for about 95 years. While still in use, it is gradually being replaced by the new dry method discussed below.

Currency is wet printed on flatbed presses, presently in sheets of 18 subjects. The paper first arrives from the contractor in mill-wet condition, ready for printing. Backs are printed first, on four-plate intaglio power presses. The engraved plates are covered with an ink film by a roller attached to an ink fountain. Surplus ink on the plate surface is removed by an oscillating paper wiper which leaves the engraved design filled with ink. A polisher then removes the last thin ink film left from the initial wiping. An automatic feeder positions the sheets of currency paper on the plate one at a time. The plate then moves forward and is gripped by an impression roller which, as it revolves, presses the paper into the fine engraving lines to pick up the ink. The sheet is then lifted by an automatic take-off and delivery device and set down on a tray. This back-printed paper is stored overnight in a humidor before the same process is used for face printing the following day. Later, the printed sheets are put through a solution to lengthen the life of the currency by making it more resistant to dirt, grease and wear. A smooth, hard finish is applied by a hydraulic press, and margins are trimmed on special trimming machines.

The final operation is done on a two-color rotary press which overprints the seals, serial numbers, series year and signatures on the 18 subjects in one simultaneous operation. (Seal and serial numbers are the same color; series year and signatures are black.) Afterwards, the sheets are further trimmed, then separated into single notes by a guillotine cutting machine. Finished notes are then examined in units of one hundred each.

Dry Printing

As part of an extensive modernization program which began in 1950, eight high-speed rotary intaglio printing presses were installed during 1957. Currency is being produced on these presses from larger back and face plates, 32 notes to a sheet, by the dry intaglio process. In contrast to the wet process, this new dry process provides for a relatively high degree of dimensional stability in the paper and simplifies subsequent trimming and cutting operations.

After the backs and faces of the notes are dry printed, stacks of the 32-subject sheets are trimmed to a uniform dimension and then serial numbers, seal, series year and signatures are printed on the notes by the typographic process. A detailed examination is then made in 16-subject form ($\frac{1}{2}$ of a full-size sheet) after which the sheets are cut into stacks of individual notes. After final examination for removal of defective notes and their replacement with "star" notes, the currency is securely banded and wrapped for delivery. The entire operation of printing and processing currency in 32-subject sheets is unique in that the work is conducted in a self-contained area. This assembly line production has made all processing easier as well as enhanced security.

Postage Stamps

Aside from its printing of paper money, perhaps the work of the Bureau having the widest general appeal is the printing of postage stamps. Here the type of printing used is "intaglio," the same as for currency. Therefore, postage stamps have much the same excellence in design, general appearance, and quality as currency. They are printed from steel engraved plates made by a hand transfer process and later curved to fit the plate cylinder of the postage stamp presses, whereas paper currency is produced from both flat and cylindrical steel engraved plates made by the electrolytic process.

Most United States postage stamps are produced by the dry intaglio process on six web-fed rotary presses, five of which were purchased in 1955, and one previously manufactured according to Bureau design. Prior to the acquisition of these six presses, U. S. postage stamps had been produced only by wet intaglio printing. It is expected that all stamps will be produced by the dry process in the near future.

Postage stamps are examined and counted by hand in the same general way as currency. Since most processes in stamp production are performed automatically without handling, the sheets of finished stamps are examined individually for imperfect work which, if found, is separated from the perfect sheets. The perfect sheets are counted before they are separated into units for final processing. The concluding step in stamp production is the automatic wrapping of individual units of sheets of stamps which are then cartoned and ready for delivery to post offices throughout the United States.

———◆—◆———

THE SERIAL NUMBER SYSTEM FOR U. S. CURRENCY

The system of numbering paper money must be adequate to accommodate a large volume of notes. For security and accountability purposes, no two notes of any one type, denomination and series may have the same serial number. The serial numbers on each note have a full complement of eight digits and an alphabetical prefix and suffix letter. When necessary, ciphers are used at the left of the number to make a total of eight digits. Every note has two identical serial numbers.

*Whenever a new numbering sequence is used for United States Notes, Silver or Gold Certificates, the first note is numbered A00 000 001A; the second A00 000 002A; the hundredth A00 000 100A; the thousandth A00 001 000A; and so on through A99 999 999A. The suffix letter "A" will remain the same until a total of 25 groups of 99,999,999 notes are numbered, each group having a different *prefix* letter from A to Z. The letter "O" is omitted, either as a prefix or as a suffix, because of its similarity to zero. The 100,000,000th note in each group will be a star note, since eight digits are the maximum practicable in the mechanical operation of the numbering machines.

At this point, the *suffix* letter changes to "B" for the next 25 groups of 99,999,999 notes, and numbering proceeds the same as with suffix letter "A." A total of 62,500,000,000 notes could be numbered before a duplication of serial numbers would occur. However, the Bureau has never been required to number that many notes of any one type, denomination and series.

The Federal Reserve Notes printed for the twelve Districts are numbered the same way as United States Notes and Silver Certificates, except that the letter identifying each District is used as a *prefix* letter at the beginning of the two serial numbers, and it does not change. Only the suffix letter changes in the serial numbers on Federal Reserve currency.

The numbering system used for National Currency and Federal Reserve Bank Notes is described in detail and illustrated with sheets on pages 92-93.

*Serial numbers start from the beginning when a completely new issue and series date is printed. For minor changes within a series date, the numbers usually continue undisturbed. This is not always the case; as an instance, the $1 Silver Certificate Series 1957 has numbers starting from the beginning, but the *same* is true for the Series 1957 A notes as well.

STAR OR REPLACEMENT NOTES

As mentioned previously on page 12, if during the course of examination a note is found to be imperfect, it is removed and replaced by a "star" note. Star notes are exactly the same as regular notes except that an independent series of serial numbers is assigned. Instead of the usual prefix letter, a star appears with the serial numbers on United States Notes and Silver Certificates; on Federal Reserve Notes the star appears in place of the suffix letter since the prefix letter is the Bank letter as well.

As explained on page 13, the 100,000,000th note of any group will also be a star note because the numbering machines are not geared to print over eight digits.

THE SERIES YEAR ON U. S. CURRENCY

The series year which appears on the face of each note signifies the year in which the design was adopted. The series year does not change each calendar year; it changes only when the basic design has a major revision. The capital letter often found following the series year indicates that a minor change was authorized in a particular currency. Minor revisions usually occur when a new Secretary or Treasurer is appointed.

The series year appears twice on older printings of modern U. S. currency. More recent issues carry this designation only once.

Series Year Appearing on All Issues of Modern-Size Notes

Since 1929, the year modern-size currency was first issued into circulation, the Bureau of Engraving has printed and delivered the following series of notes:

UNITED STATES NOTES

Denomination	Series
$1	1928
$2	1928, 1928 A, 1928 B, 1928 C, 1928 D, 1928 E, 1928 F, 1928 G, 1953, 1953 A, 1953 B and 1963.
$5	1928, 1928 A, 1928 B, 1928 C, 1928 D, 1928 E, 1928 F, 1953, 1953 A, 1953 B, 1953 C and 1963.

SILVER CERTIFICATES

Denomination	Series
$1	1928, 1928 A, 1928 B, 1928 C, 1928 D, 1928 E, 1934, 1935, 1935 A, 1935 B, 1935 C, 1935 D, 1935 E, 1935 F, 1935 G, 1935 H, 1957, 1957 A and 1957 B.
$5	1934, 1934 A, 1934 B, 1934 C, 1934 D, 1953, 1953 A, 1953 B and 1953 C.
$10	1933, 1933 A, 1934, 1934 A, 1934 B, 1934 C, 1934 D, 1953, 1953 A and 1953 B.

NATIONAL BANK NOTES

Denomination	*Series*
$5, $10, $20, $50 and $100	1929.

FEDERAL RESERVE BANK NOTES

Denomination	*Series*
$5, $10, $20, $50 and $100	1929.

FEDERAL RESERVE NOTES

Denomination	*Series*
$1	1963.
$5	1928, 1928 A, 1928 B, 1928 C, 1928 D, 1934, 1934 A, 1934 B, 1934 C, 1934 D, 1950, 1950 A, 1950 B, 1950 C, 1950 D and 1963.
$10 and $20	1928, 1928 A, 1928 B, 1928 C, 1934, 1934 A, 1934 B, 1934 C, 1934 D, 1950, 1950 A, 1950 B, 1950 C, 1950 D and 1963.
$50 and $100	1928, 1928 A, 1934, 1934 A, 1934 B, 1934 C, 1950, 1950 A, 1950 B, 1950 C and 1950 D.
$500, $1,000, $5,000 and $10,000	1928, 1934 and 1934 A.

GOLD CERTIFICATES

Denomination	*Series*
$10 and $20	1928 and 1928 A.
$50, $500 and $5,000	1928.
$100, $1,000 and $10,000	1928 and 1934.
$100,000	1934.

THE TREASURY SEAL

The Treasury Seal now imprinted on the face of all U. S. currency is older than the Constitution. On September 25, 1778, the Continental Congress appointed a committee composed of John Witherspoon, Gouverneur Morris and Richard Henry Lee to design a seal. In the Journals of Congress of that date is a resolution providing "that the Comptroller shall keep the Treasury books and seal . . . shall draw bills under said seal." The resulting design was submitted and approved, and the Seal is found on official documents dating back to 1782. It was retained after the ratification of the Constitution in 1788.

Through the years, the design of the Seal has remained basically the same though minor changes were effected in 1849 when a new die was prepared. (A third die was made by the Bureau of Engraving in 1915, and is in use at the present time.) The design includes a shield on which appear a balance scale representing Justice and a key which symbolizes official authority. They are separated by a chevron bearing 13 stars for the 13 original colonies or states. The shield is surrounded by a spray of laurel in blossom. The following Latin legend surrounds the shield: THESAUR. AMER. SEPTENT SIGIL.

Written out, this is "Thesauri Americae Septentrionalis Sigillum," meaning "The Seal of the Treasury of North America." There is no reverse to the Treasury Seal.

The Seal is imprinted on official Treasury documents and on the face side of U. S. currency beginning with the first issue of Legal Tender Notes authorized in 1862. The Demand Note series 1861 and the first three issues of Fractional Currency constitute the only U. S. paper money which does not bear the Treasury Seal.

THE GREAT SEAL OF THE UNITED STATES

On August 15, 1935, the Treasury Department announced that production of a new $1.00 Silver Certificate had begun. The design chosen for the new back was the Great Seal of the United States. This was the first time both sides of the Great Seal were to appear on any U. S. money.*

The obverse of the Great Seal is the familiar American eagle with a shield, holding an olive branch in one talon and arrows in the other. Above are thirteen stars and the Latin motto "E Pluribus Unum."

The reverse of the Great Seal shows an unfinished pyramid, surmounted by an eye in a triangular glory. The pyramid bears in Roman numerals the year of the Declaration of Independence, 1776. Above the eye is the Latin motto "Annuit Coeptis," rendered as "He (God) favored our undertakings." The motto at the bottom is "Novus Ordo Seclorum" and is translated as "A new order of the ages." The eye and triangular glory represent an all-seeing Deity. The pyramid is the symbol of strength; its unfinished condition denotes the belief of the Seal's designers that there was yet work to be done. Both mottoes on the reverse are condensations of excerpts from Virgil's Aeneid.

The first committee on the Great Seal was formed on the afternoon of July 4, 1776, and consisted of Benjamin Franklin, Thomas Jefferson and John Adams. The Great Seal as finally adopted was largely the work of Charles Thomson, Secretary of Congress, and William Barton, a private citizen of Philadelphia. The design was officially adopted on June 20, 1782, by Fundamental Law. The Great Seal was again ratified after the Constitution was adopted in 1789.

According to Treasury records, the only previous use of the reverse of the Great Seal was in 1882, when a centennial medal was issued by the United States mint to celebrate the 100th anniversary of the Great Seal's adoption.

*Further details concerning the adoption of this design, including illustrations of models before and after approval, are contained in the *History of the Bureau of Engraving and Printing,* pages 121-123.

THE NATIONAL MOTTO ON U. S. CURRENCY

An Act of Congress approved by the President on July 11, 1955, authorized the appearance of the National Motto on all U. S. currency. The first notes to bear the motto were $1 Silver Certificates Series 1957, which were released to circulation on October 1 of that year.

The changeover is being implemented gradually, as the Bureau installs new high-speed rotary presses using the dry-print method to produce sheets of 32 subjects. At present, most low-denomination notes are being produced with the motto. It is expected that some time during 1965, the higher denominations will also be printed with the motto.

TREASURY OFFICIALS
AND THEIR TERMS OF OFFICE

Modern U. S. currency is very often collected by signature combination. These facsimile signatures appeared on currency made (but not necessarily all issued) during the respective tenures of office of the various Treasury officials. The National Currency and Federal Reserve Bank Notes Series of 1929 used the Register-Treasurer signatures; all the rest from the first issues series dated 1928 to the present show the Treasurer-Secretary combination. It is understandable that notes bearing signatures of officials who served a short term together will be more difficult to find than those bearing signatures of officials who were in office for a long concurrent term.

Chart of Concurrent Terms of Office

Following is a chart showing the length of time the various signatories of modern U. S. currency have held concurrent office:

Treasurer–Secretary	First Day	Last Day	Years Months Days
H. T. Tate–A. W. Mellon	Apr. 30, 1928	Jan. 17, 1929	00/08/17
W. O. Woods–A. W. Mellon	Jan. 18, 1929	Feb. 12, 1932	03/00/25
W. O. Woods–Ogden L. Mills	Feb. 13, 1932	Mar. 3, 1933	01/00/18
W. O. Woods–W. H. Woodin	Mar. 4, 1933	May 31, 1933	00/02/27
W. A. Julian–W. H. Woodin	June 1, 1933	Dec. 31, 1933	00/07/00
W. A. Julian–Henry Morgenthau, Jr	Jan. 1, 1934	July 22, 1945	11/06/22
W. A. Julian–Fred M. Vinson	July 23, 1945	July 23, 1946	01/00/00
W. A. Julian–John W. Snyder	July 25, 1946	May 29, 1949	02/10/04
Georgia Neese Clarke–John W. Snyder	June 21, 1949	Jan. 20, 1953	03/07/00
Ivy Baker Priest–G. M. Humphrey	Jan. 28, 1953	July 28, 1957	04/06/00
Ivy Baker Priest–Robert B. Anderson	July 29, 1957	Jan. 20, 1961	03/05/23
Elizabeth Rudel Smith–C. Douglas Dillon	Jan. 30, 1961	Apr. 13, 1962	01/03/14
Kathryn O'Hay Granahan–C. Douglas Dillon	Currently in office.		
Register–Treasurer			
E. E. Jones–W. O. Woods	Jan. 22, 1929	May 31, 1933	04/04/09

When the Treasurer or Secretary, or both, leave office and a new official is appointed, a letter is added after the series date and of course the signatures are changed. Originally these signatures were engraved on the face plates, which then had to be discarded upon the appearance of a new official. In recent years the signatures (along with other numbers and symbols) have been overprinted, beginning with the following series:

SILVER CERTIFICATES	UNITED STATES NOTES
$1 Series 1935	$2 Series 1953
$5 Series 1953	$5 Series 1953
$10 Series 1953	

FEDERAL RESERVE NOTES
All — Series 1950

GRADING OF CURRENCY

The Following Grades of Condition are Used in the
Catalog Section of this Book

NEW — A note that is as clean and crisp as the day it was printed. Such a note may have been obtained directly from a bank teller, or it may have passed through several careful hands. New bills have no folds or creases. Minor flaws or signs of careless handling are at times found on new notes right out of a bank pack. Such notes may be described as new but the flaws must be mentioned.

EXTRA FINE — A note that is almost new, with very minor creases which have not impaired the design and appearance of the note. It must not have cuts, tears or discoloration, and should still be quite crisp. A note that has been washed cannot be considered Extra Fine.

VERY FINE — A note showing slight evidence of circulation. It may have light folds or creases, but will still retain some of its original feel and appearance. The note might have been carefully cleaned or pressed, but this process must not have impaired the appearance of the vignette.

FINE — A note which shows considerable use but is completely legible and not torn or stained. The note will have lost its crispness and may show a little edge wear. It may also have been more heavily creased or folded.

Introduction to the Catalog

During 1964, the Bureau of Engraving finished the compilation of records showing the amounts delivered of each note by denomination, type and series. Figures showing these totals are incorporated in the body of the catalog itself. The rest (dates of issue, serial numbers and other pertinent data) is included as Appendix B.

Detailed files relative to the adoption of modern-size United States currency have also been maintained by the Bureau. The most important excerpts, which include Secretary MacVeagh's official order of 1913 to reduce the size of U. S. currency, will be found as Appendix A.

A number of small discrepancies were found in the Bureau's material; these have been carefully corrected where it seemed logical to do so. No attempt was made to insert individual totals where such figures could not be supplied by the Bureau. Many separate totals are not available for the earlier issues, as the records kept made no distinction between series variations. Where such was the case, proper annotations have been inserted. There is also one issue which exists though Bureau records have nothing to indicate that it was ever printed. A few others of similar nature may exist and are so mentioned in their respective listings.

For the sake of continuity all notes of every type and denomination issued for general circulation are included in this section, though notes higher than the $100 denomination carry no price valuation.

One of the main features of this catalog is the use of the new Donlon Simplified Numbering System. Each note is given a specific number according to its type, denomination, series date and variety. A detailed explanation of this system follows:

THE DONLON SIMPLIFIED NUMBERING SYSTEM

All modern United States currency from $1 to $10,000 is included in this Numbering System. Actually the numbering is in a form of code. The first three digits of the reference number assigned to a note quickly identify its *Type* and *Denomination*.

The *Type* is indicated by the *First Digit* as follows:

1 — UNITED STATES NOTE
2 — SILVER CERTIFICATE
3 — NATIONAL CURRENCY
4 — FEDERAL RESERVE BANK NOTE
5 — FEDERAL RESERVE NOTE
6 — GOLD CERTIFICATE

The *Denomination* is shown by the *Second* and *Third* digits:

01 — ONE DOLLAR
02 — TWO DOLLARS
05 — FIVE DOLLARS
10 — TEN DOLLARS
20 — TWENTY DOLLARS
50 — FIFTY DOLLARS
00 — ONE HUNDRED DOLLARS

For notes over $100, the following *number-letter* scheme will apply:

500 — FIVE HUNDRED DOLLARS
1M — ONE THOUSAND DOLLARS
5M — FIVE THOUSAND DOLLARS
10M — TEN THOUSAND DOLLARS

A numeral (usually one digit) to indicate the *Series* follows those for type and denomination. The series order is given for notes in the exact sequence of release, which is not necessarily chronological.

A suffix letter corresponding with District letters, A to L, is used for Federal Reserve Notes and Federal Reserve Bank Notes.

Breaking down the full number in reading may prove helpful in utilizing the Numbering System. Examples:

101	One-0-One	United States Note, $1
205	Two-0-Five	Silver Certificate, $5
310	Three-Ten	National Currency, $10
420A	Four-Twenty-A	Federal Reserve Bank Note, $20, Boston District
5-10M-1B	Five-Ten-M-One-B	Federal Reserve Note, $10,000, 1st Series, New York District
650	Six-Fifty	Gold Certificate, $50

This numbering system allows for any new notes to be added very easily by using the various numbers and letters that apply to the new issue.

UNITED STATES NOTES — Red Seal

United States Notes, also known as Legal Tender Notes or Greenbacks, were first authorized by the Act of Congress of February 25, 1862. Denominations for the large-size notes ranged from $1 to $10,000. Modern-size notes presently consist of only the $2 and $5 denominations;* there was an issue of $1 notes series dated 1928 which is now obsolete.

When finished, United States Notes are delivered to a vault under custody of the Treasurer of the United States. As required by the Act of May 31, 1878, and the recently enacted Old Series Currency Adjustment Act, the amount outstanding is kept at $322,681,016. The Treasury holds a reserve in gold of $156,039,431 to back these notes. The seal and serial numbers are in red.

The following notations will clarify certain aspects of various issues:

Series of 1928 — The legal tender clause on earlier issues of this type reads, "This Note Is A Legal Tender at its Face Value For All Debts Public and Private Except Duties on Imports and Interest on the Public Debt."

Series of 1928 B — The Act of May 12, 1933 removed legal tender restrictions from all U. S. money, and the clause on $5.00 notes of this type was changed as follows: "This Note Is A Legal Tender at its Face Value For All Debts Public and Private." For $2.00 notes, this change began with Series of 1928 C issues. All subsequent printings up to Series 1963 carry this same clause.

Series of 1928 C — For $5 notes, the Face Plate Number appears in larger-size numerals on this and succeeding issues. For $2 notes this begins with Series of 1928 D.

Series 1953 — Along with a general rearrangement of the face side, the following changes occurred on this and succeeding issues:

Series designation appears only once, and the word "OF" is deleted.

The Treasury seal and serial numbers are reduced in size.

Signatures are overprinted instead of engraved.

Series 1963 — The addition of the motto to the backs of United States Notes took place in 1963, along with the changeover in printing method from wet to dry and increase in number of subjects per sheet from 18 to 32. The new legal tender clause reads, "This Note is Legal Tender For All Debts, Public and Private." The "Will Pay . . ." clause, near the bottom of the face side on previous issues, no longer appears on the notes.

*10 and $20 plates were made, as a specimen of each (Series of 1928, Woods-Mills) was in the Treasury's currency exhibit at the Chicago World's Fair 1933-1934.

101 One Dollar, Portrait of Washington

Face Design 101-1

$1.00 & $2.00 UNITED STATES NOTES

Back Design 101-1; 201-1 through 7

No.	Series	Treasurer-Secretary	Delivered	V. Fine	Ex. Fine	New
101-1	1928	Woods-Woodin..........1,872,012	$10.00	$15.00	$30.00

102 Two Dollars, Portrait of Jefferson

Face Design 102-1 through 8

Back Design 102-1 through 12

[21]

$2.00 UNITED STATES NOTES

No.	Series	Treasurer-Secretary	Delivered	V. Fine	Ex. Fine	New
102-1	1928	Tate-Mellon.....................		$10.00	$ 30.00	$ 45.00
102-2	1928 A	Woods-Mellon..................		15.00	35.00	60.00
102-3	1928 B	Woods-Mills...................		50.00	150.00	250.00
102-4	1928 C	Julian-Morgenthau..............		7.50	12.00	22.50
102-5	1928 D	Julian-Morgenthau..............		6.00	10.00	20.00
102-6	1928 E	Julian-Vinson............6,480,000		8.00	15.00	27.50
102-7	1928 F	Julian-Snyder..........42,360,000		4.00	8.00	15.00
102-8	1928 G	Clarke-Snyder.........52,208,000		3.50	5.00	9.00

Total issue 329,712,000 for Nos. 102-1 through 102-5. No breakdown is available as to exact number printed and delivered of each of these notes. Valuations reflect relative scarcity.

Face Design 102-9 through 12

No.	Series	Treasurer-Secretary	Delivered	V. Fine	Ex. Fine	New
102-9	1953	Priest-Humphrey.......45,360,000		....	4.00	7.50
102-10	1953 A	Priest-Anderson.........18,000,000		....	4.00	8.00
102-11	1953 B	Smith-Dillon...........10,800,000		....	....	5.00
102-12	1953 C	Granahan-Dillon.........5,760,000		....	....	4.50

Face Design 102-13

No.	Series	Treasurer-Secretary	Delivered	V. Fine	Ex. Fine	New
102-13	1963	Granahan-Dillon..........Current		....	....	3.50

$2.00 & $5.00 UNITED STATES NOTES

Back Design 102-13

105   Five Dollars, Portrait of Lincoln

Face Design 105-1 through 7

Back Design 105-1 through 11; 205-1 through 9; A205; 305; 405; 505-1A through 15L.

$5.00 UNITED STATES NOTES

No.	Series	Treasurer-Secretary	Delivered	V. Fine	Ex. Fine	New
105-1	1928	Woods-Mellon...................		$10.00	$30.00	$45.00
105-2	1928 A	Woods-Mills....................		15.00	37.50	70.00
105-3	1928 B	Julian-Morgenthau...............		10.00	20.00	35.00
105-4	1928 C	Julian-Morgenthau...............		9.00	15.00	27.50
105-5	1928 D	Julian-Vinson...........11,868,000		12.00	32.50	50.00
105-6	1928 E	Julian-Snyder.........109,096,000		9.00	15.00	25.00
105-7	1928 F	Clarke-Snyder.........107,876,000		8.00	12.00	22.50

Total issue 650,628,000 for Nos. 105-1 through 105-4. No breakdown is available as to exact number printed and delivered of each of these notes. Valuations reflect relative scarcity.

Face Design 105-8 through 11

No.	Series	Treasurer-Secretary	Delivered	V. Fine	Ex. Fine	New
105-8	1953	Priest-Humphrey.......120,880,000	....		8.00	17.50
105-9	1953 A	Priest-Anderson.........90,280,000	....		8.00	17.50
105-10	1953 B	Smith-Dillon...........44,640,000	....		7.50	15.00
105-11	1953 C	Granahan-Dillon.........8,640,000	....		....	10.00

Face Design 105-12

$5.00 UNITED STATES NOTES

Back Design 105-12; 505-16

No.	Series	Treasurer-Secretary	Delivered	V. Fine	Ex. Fine	New
105-12	1963	Granahan-Dillon . . . . Current		....	....	$8.50

——◆—◆——

SILVER CERTIFICATES — Blue Seal

Certificates backed by silver dollars were first authorized by the Bland-Allison Act of February 28, 1878. Large-size notes were made in denominations from $1 to $1000 at various intervals.

Modern-size Silver Certificates were first released on July 10, 1929, series dated 1928, and constituted practically all the $1 notes issued over a period of years. At first, these were also backed by silver dollars; their wording referred to their redemption in "One Silver Dollar" as had all previous issues of Silver Certificates. All this was changed by the Silver Purchase Act of 1934, which allowed for such certificates to be issued against any standard silver dollars, silver, or silver bullion held by the Treasury. Accordingly, the wording in the redemption clause was changed to read "One Dollar in Silver," allowing for the option of redemption in silver dollars or bullion.

On March 25, 1964, Secretary of the Treasury Dillon halted the outflow of silver dollars, stating that thenceforth silver bullion would be used for the redemption of Silver Certificates presented for that purpose.

Modern-size Silver Certificates were made only in the $1, $5 and $10 denominations. Upon completion they were delivered to a vault under the custody of the Treasurer of the United States. However, Silver Certificates are no longer being printed, as they were abolished by the Act of June 4, 1963 (at which time Federal Reserve $1 and $2 notes were authorized).

The seal and serial numbers are in blue.

The following explanatory notes will clarify differences and series date changes found on these notes:

Series of 1928 — The legal tender clause first read, "This Certificate is Receivable For All Public Dues and When So Received May Be Reissued."

Series of 1933 — Pursuant to the Act of May 12, 1933, a new series of Silver Certificates was initiated. Issued only in the $10 denomination, this is one of the most desirable and unique notes in the modern U.S. currency series. It is in fact a "Silver Coin Note," so stated on the face side. Its legal tender clause is as follows: "This Certificate is Issued Pursuant to Section 16 of the Act of May 12, 1933, and is Legal Tender at its Face Value For All Debts Public and Private."

SILVER CERTIFICATES

Series of 1934 — The Act of June 19, 1934 necessitated further change in the legal tender clause; it was altered on the Series of 1934 notes and for the remainder of Silver Certificate issues, reading as follows: "This Certificate is Legal Tender For All Debts, Public and Private." On $1 notes, the Treasury seal was moved to the right side and a large blue numeral 1 was added on the left.

Series of 1934 A — Numerals in the Face Plate Number are larger on this and succeeding issues of $5 and $10 notes.

Series 1935 — The word "OF" was deleted from the series designation on these $1 notes and succeeding series dates. "Series 1935" appears twice on the face. Also, the large word "ONE" at the right is removed, and the numeral 1 at the left is gray instead of blue.

Series 1935 A — The size of the numerals in the Face Plate Number was made larger, and the series designation appears only once on this and succeeding issues of $1 notes.

   Aside from issues for regular circulation, notes from this series were used as part of the special **HAWAII** overprint and Yellow Seal North Africa emissions of World War II.

Series 1953 — The following changes took place on the face side of this and succeeding issues of $5 and $10 notes:

   Series designation appears only once, and the word "OF" is deleted.
   Signatures are overprinted instead of engraved.
   The Treasury seal and serial numbers are reduced in size.
   The numeral at the left is gray instead of blue.

Series 1957 — For the first time the motto appears on U.S. currency. Also, printings of 32-subject sheets begin with this series.

201   One Dollar, Portrait of Washington

Face Design 201-1 through 6. Back Design on page 21.

No.	Series	Treasurer-Secretary	Delivered	V. Fine	Ex. Fine	New
201-1	1928	Tate-Mellon....................		$ 6.50	$ 12.50	$ 25.00
201-2	1928 A	Woods-Mellon.......		4.00	7.50	12.50
201-3	1928 B	Woods-Mills....................		4.50	8.00	15.00
201-4	1928 C	Woods-Woodin.................		50.00	110.00	175.00
201-5	1928 D	Julian-Woodin.................		40.00	90.00	150.00
201-6	1928 E	Julian-Morgenthau.............		60.00	175.00	300.00

Total issue 3,487,020,000 for Nos. 201-1 through 201-6. Bureau records do not contain a breakdown for each of these notes separately. Valuations reflect relative scarcity.

$1.00 SILVER CERTIFICATES

Face Design 201-7. Back Design on page 21.

No.	Series	Treasurer-Secretary	Delivered	V. Fine	Ex. Fine	New
201-7	1934	Julian-Morgenthau.....682,176,000		$2.50	$7.50	$17.50

Face Design 201-8; General Face Design 201-9 through 20; A201.

201-8	1935	Julian-Morgenthau....1,681,552,000	2.00	5.00		15.00
201-9	1935 A	Julian-Morgenthau....6,111,832,000	....	2.50		6.00
201-10	1935 B	Julian-Vinson.........806,612,000	2.25	6.50		15.00
201-11	1935 C	Julian-Snyder........3,088,108,000	....	3.00		7.50
†201-12W	1935 D	Clarke-Snyder ⎫ 4,656,968,000	....	2.50		6.50
†201-12N	1935 D	Clarke-Snyder ⎭	....	2.50		5.00
201-13	1935 E	Priest-Humphrey.....5,134,056,000	....	2.00		5.00
*201-14	1957	Priest-Anderson......2,609,600,000	....	....		2.50
201-15	1935 F	Priest-Anderson......1,173,360,000	....	1.50		4.50
*201-16	1957 A	Smith-Dillon.........1,594,080,000	....	....		2.50
201-17	1935 G	Smith-Dillon..........194,600,000	....	....		4.00
*201-18	1935 G	Smith-Dillon...........31,320,000	....	1.50		4.50
*201-19	1957 B	Granahan-Dillon......718,400,000	....	....		2.00
*201-20	1935 H	Granahan-Dillon.......30,520,000	....	....		3.50

The 1935 D series was printed in sheets of 12 and 18 subjects:

    4,510,024,000 in sheets of 12 notes

    146,944,000 in sheets of 18 notes

    4,656,968,000 Total 1935 D notes

*With Motto "In God We Trust." 1935 G comes with and without the Motto.

†Wide and Narrow Designs — See explanation on following page.

$1.00 SILVER CERTIFICATES
The "Great Seal" Back Design

Back Design 201-8 through 12W; A201

Back Design 201-12N, 13, 15, 17

There are two varieties of backs for Series 1935 D notes known as Wide and Narrow designs. The Wide design is about $\frac{1}{16}$ inch wider, easily recognized when compared with the Narrow design. The most obvious area for comparison is the "cobweb" border under ONE DOLLAR.

The Narrow design was used for subsequent issues of the 1935 series.

Back Design 201-14, 16, 18, 19, 20; 501-1A through 1L

[28]

$5.00 SILVER CERTIFICATES

205 Five Dollars, Portrait of Lincoln

Face Design 205-1 through 5; A205. Back Design on page 23.

No.	Series	Treasurer-Secretary	Delivered	Ex. Fine	New
205-1	1934	Julian-Morgenthau	350,352,000	$12.50	$30.00
205-2	1934 A	Julian-Morgenthau	740,128,000	10.00	25.00
205-3	1934 B	Julian-Vinson	60,328,000	22.50	60.00
205-4	1934 C	Julian-Snyder	372,328,000	7.00	22.50
205-5	1934 D	Clarke-Snyder	491,660,000	....	20.00

Face Design 205-6 through 9. Back Design on page 23.

205-6	1953	Priest-Humphrey	339,600,000	....	17.50
205-7	1953 A	Priest-Anderson	232,400,000	....	15.00
205-8	1953 B	Smith-Dillon	73,000,000	....	8.00
205-9	1953 C	Granahan-Dillon		Not Released	

[29]

$10.00 SILVER CERTIFICATES

210 Ten Dollars, Portrait of Hamilton

Face Design 210-1

Back Design 210-1 through 9; A210; 310; 410; 510-1A through 15L; 610-1 and 2.

No.	Series	Treasurer-Secretary	Delivered	V. Fine	Ex. Fine	New
210-1	1933	Julian-Woodin.............216,000		$90.00	$275.00	$500.00
‡**210-1a**	1933 A	Julian-Morgenthau.........336,000			unknown	

‡ The reason the $10 No. 210-1a is presently unknown is found in a letter written by former Bureau Director A. W. Hall on April 3, 1941, in which he stated, ". . . in regard to the $10 silver certificates, series of 1933 and 1933-A, you are advised that a total of 552,000 of the two were delivered to the Treasurer of the United States in 1934. Of this number at least 300,000 were series 1933-A.

"Of the number delivered to the Treasurer, 184,000 were issued between January and August, 1934, and the remainder, 368,000, were destroyed in November, 1935. Whether any 1933-A's were among those issued apparently cannot be determined. However, as the 1933 plate was first at press, it is possible that all the certificates issued were from this plate."

This letter appeared in *The Numismatist,* June, 1941, and was addressed to Mr. Robert H. Lloyd.

$10.00 SILVER CERTIFICATES

Face Design 210-2 through 6; A210

No.	Series	Treasurer-Secretary	Delivered	V. Fine	Ex. Fine	New
210-2	1934	Julian-Morgenthau 9,132,000	. . . .	$ 35.00	$ 65.00
210-3	1934 A	Julian-Morgenthau 106,300,000	. . . .	22.50	40.00
210-4	1934 B	Julian-Vinson 1,416,000	$90.00	275.00	400.00
210-5	1934 C	Julian-Snyder 21,718,000	. . . .	12.50	20.00
210-6	1934 D	Clarke-Snyder 11,630,000	. . . .	15.00	30.00

Face Design 210-7 through 9

No.	Series	Treasurer-Secretary	Delivered	V. Fine	Ex. Fine	New
210-7	1953	Priest-Humphrey 10,440,000	. . . .	12.50	25.00
210-8	1953 A	Priest-Anderson 1,080,000	. . . .	15.00	27.50
210-9	1953 B	Smith-Dillon 720,000	. . . .	12.50	20.00

[31]

NATIONAL CURRENCY — Brown Seal

National Currency was first authorized by the National Banking Act of 1863, superseded by the National Currency Act of June 3, 1864. This Act provided for the establishment of national banks and the issuance of circulating notes. These notes were to be secured by United States interest-bearing registered bonds deposited with the Treasurer, upon which the banks could receive 90% of current market value in notes.

Modern-size National Currency was first issued on July 15, 1929. Unusual features of this issue include the use of the Register-Treasurer signature combination (instead of Secretary-Treasurer as found on most other modern-size notes) and the series date which is 1929. The printing plates for the face side are also quite different from other modern-size types. The engraved borders are reduced in proportion and size to make room for the imprinting of bank names, locations, charter numbers and names of bank officials. All these details were printed by a logotype process onto the notes; since so many different banks issued such notes a great saving was thus made in the preparation of plates. The backs are uniform with other modern types.

There are two distinct types of modern-size National Currency. Type One, issued from July 1929 to May 1933, has the bank's charter number in two places, in black. National Currency was printed 12 notes to a sheet and delivered in vertical sheets of six. For Type One, each of these six notes had the same serial numbers and suffix letter but a different prefix letter, A through F, which served to denote its position on the vertical sheet.

Type Two notes were issued from May 1933 to May 1935. These bore consecutive serial numbers, the suffix letters were dropped and the charter number of the bank was added twice more, in thinner brown numerals. Thus, the charter number appears four times on Type Two notes — twice in black logotype and twice in brown as described. Both Types are illustrated in sheets on page 92. Type Two notes are much scarcer than those of Type One.

National Currency is usually collected by states or by cities or banks with odd names, places of historical interest, and by low charter numbers or low or unusual serial numbers. $50 and $100 notes are often collected as single examples because of their high face value. No notes of these two denominations were issued from Alabama, Alaska, Arizona, Arkansas, Georgia, Maine, New Mexico, South Carolina or Utah.

Throughout the years National Bank Notes were in use, various amendments were made affecting their circulation and redemption. Provisions were made for the transfer of redemption liability from the separate banks to the United States, which now cancels and retires any National Bank Notes that are turned in.

National Currency became obsolete on May 20, 1935, as bonds matured or were otherwise declared ineligible for security purposes.

The redemption clause on these notes reads as follows: "Redeemable in Lawful Money of the United States at United States Treasury or at the Bank of Issue." The seal and serial numbers are in brown.

Valuations are at best a guide to general availability. Some states are very difficult to obtain, others may have one issue commonly available but very scarce otherwise, one denomination from a state may be easily available and another very hard to find. The table on page 33 lists the states alphabetically with their respective rarity ratings. Values follow accordingly.

NATIONAL CURRENCY

TABLE OF RARITY

Valuations following the Table of Rarity are based on this list:

State	Rarity	State	Rarity
Alabama	4	Montana	6
Alaska	9	Nebraska	3
Arizona	7	Nevada	7
Arkansas	5	New Hampshire	4
California	3	New Jersey	2
Colorado	3	New Mexico	8
Connecticut	2	New York	1
Delaware	5	North Carolina	4
District of Columbia	5	North Dakota	4
Florida	5	Ohio	1
Georgia	4	Oklahoma	5
Hawaii	8	Oregon	6
Idaho	6	Pennsylvania	1
Illinois	1	Rhode Island	5
Indiana	1	South Carolina	4
Iowa	2	South Dakota	5
Kansas	3	Tennessee	3
Kentucky	3	Texas	2
Louisiana	6	Utah	7
Maine	4	Vermont	4
Maryland	3	Virginia	3
Massachusetts	1	Washington	6
Michigan	1	West Virginia	3
Minnesota	2	Wisconsin	2
Mississippi	5	Wyoming	6
Missouri	2		

Five Dollars, Portrait of Lincoln

Face Design 305-1 (Type 1). Back Design on page 23.

[33]

$5.00 & $10.00 NATIONAL CURRENCY

Face Design 305-2 (Type 2). Back Design on page 23.

305-1 TYPE ONE, and 305-2 TYPE TWO

Rarity	Fine	Very Fine	Extra Fine	New
1........	$ 9.00	$12.00	$ 17.50	$ 25.00
2........	9.00	12.00	20.00	30.00
3........	9.00	12.00	22.50	32.50
4........	10.00	15.00	25.00	35.00
5........	12.50	17.50	30.00	40.00
6........	12.50	18.50	32.50	50.00
7........	17.50	22.50	45.00	65.00
8........	22.50	32.50	75.00	125.00
9........	25.00	40.00	100.00	150.00

Ten Dollars, Portrait of Hamilton

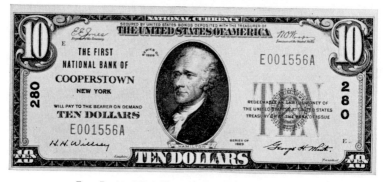

Face Design 310-1 (Type 1). Back Design on page 30.

$10.00 & $20.00 NATIONAL CURRENCY

Face Design 310-2 (Type 2). Back Design on page 30.

310-1 TYPE ONE, and 310-2 TYPE TWO

Rarity	Fine	Very Fine	Extra Fine	New
1........	$13.50	$17.50	$ 22.50	$ 32.50
2........	13.50	17.50	22.50	35.00
3........	13.50	17.50	25.00	37.50
4........	15.00	20.00	27.50	42.50
5........	15.00	22.50	30.00	45.00
6........	17.50	25.00	35.00	55.00
7........	22.50	27.50	45.00	75.00
8........	30.00	35.00	75.00	125.00
9........	35.00	42.50	100.00	150.00

Twenty Dollars, Portrait of Jackson

Face Design 320-1 (Type 1). Back Design on page 59.

$20.00 & $50.00 NATIONAL CURRENCY

Face Design 320-2 (Type 2). Back Design on page 59.

320-1 TYPE ONE, and 320-2 TYPE TWO

Rarity	Fine	Very Fine	Extra Fine	New
1.......	$22.50	$25.00	$ 30.00	$ 42.50
2.......	22.50	25.00	32.50	45.00
3.......	25.00	27.50	35.00	47.50
4.......	25.00	30.00	37.50	50.00
5.......	27.50	32.50	40.00	55.00
6.......	30.00	35.00	47.50	65.00
7.......	35.00	40.00	60.00	85.00
8.......	37.50	50.00	100.00	150.00
9.......	45.00	60.00	125.00	175.00

Fifty Dollars, Portrait of Grant

Face Design 350-1 (Type 1). Back Design on page 66.

$50 & $100 NATIONAL CURRENCY

350-1 TYPE ONE, and **350-2** TYPE TWO

Rarity	Fine	Very Fine	Extra Fine	New
1........	$60.00	$ 70.00	$ 80.00	$110.00
2........	62.50	75.00	90.00	115.00
3........	65.00	80.00	100.00	125.00
4........	67.50	85.00	110.00	130.00
5........	70.00	90.00	115.00	140.00
6........	75.00	100.00	120.00	150.00
7........	80.00	110.00	125.00	175.00
8........	90.00	120.00	150.00	200.00

One Hundred Dollars, Portrait of Franklin

Face Design 300-1 (Type I). Back Design on page 72.

300-1 TYPE ONE, and **300-2** TYPE TWO

1........	110.00	125.00	150.00	175.00
2........	115.00	130.00	155.00	180.00
3........	120.00	135.00	160.00	190.00
4........	125.00	150.00	175.00	200.00
5........	130.00	155.00	180.00	210.00
6........	135.00	165.00	210.00	250.00
7........	140.00	175.00	225.00	275.00
8........	150.00	180.00	250.00	300.00

[37]

FEDERAL RESERVE BANK NOTES — Brown Seal

Federal Reserve Bank Notes were first authorized by the Act of December 23, 1913, which established the Federal Reserve System. Unlike Federal Reserve Notes, these Bank Notes were not obligations of the United States. Rather, they were obligations of the specific Federal Reserve Banks appearing on the face.

Modern-size Federal Reserve Bank Notes were authorized by the Act of March 9, 1933. This Act permitted Federal Reserve Banks to issue currency equal to 100% of the face value of United States bonds, or 90% of the estimated value of commercial paper used as collateral. These Bank Notes were issued to relieve the emergency brought about by heavy withdrawals of Federal Reserve Notes in January and February of 1933.

Plates originally made for the Series of 1929 National Currency discussed on page 32 were hastily adapted and the Bank Notes were quickly prepared and issued. Naturally, these notes very closely resembled the National Currency issues: alterations were made only in the overprint on the face side. Instead of the local bank's Cashier and President signatures, there appeared the signatures of the Federal Reserve Bank's Cashier and Governor, with but three exceptions. The Cashier's signature was replaced by the Deputy Governor on New York District notes, the Assistant Deputy Governor on Chicago District notes and the Controller on the St. Louis District notes. The designated letter of each Federal Reserve Bank and District was placed on the notes in four places. The brown seal was slightly larger than that used on the National Bank notes. The words "or by like deposit of other securities" were logotyped near the top. The series date remained 1929 and the engraved signatures of Jones and Woods (Register and Treasurer) were also retained.

Serial numbers for each Federal Reserve Bank started with 00000001A, preceded by a District letter A to L used as a prefix.

Federal Reserve Bank Notes were delivered in sheets of six notes, as were the National Currency issues. Denominations included $5, $10, $20, $50, and $100. Their issuance was discontinued in July, 1935. These notes in new condition are much scarcer than realized.

The seal and serial numbers are in brown.

405   Five Dollars, Portrait of Lincoln

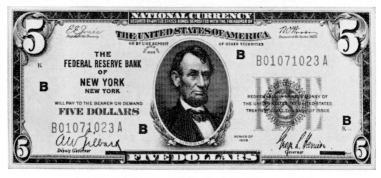

Face Design 405A through L. Back Design on page 23.

$5.00 & $10.00 FEDERAL RESERVE BANK NOTES

No.	Federal Reserve Bank	Delivered	Fine	Ex. Fine	New
405A	Boston	3,180,000	$17.50	$30.00	$ 40.00
405B	New York	2,100,000	20.00	32.50	45.00
405C	Philadelphia	3,096,000	17.50	30.00	40.00
405D	Cleveland	4,236,000	15.00	25.00	35.00
405E	Richmond	No record	....	....	....
405F	Atlanta	1,884,000	20.00	37.50	50.00
405G	Chicago	5,988,000	15.00	22.50	30.00
405H	St. Louis	276,000	45.00	90.00	125.00
405 I	Minneapolis	684,000	30.00	50.00	70.00
405J	Kansas City	2,460,000	20.00	32.50	45.00
405K	Dallas	996,000	25.00	45.00	65.00
405L	San Francisco	360,000	32.50	60.00	85.00

410   Ten Dollars, Portrait of Hamilton

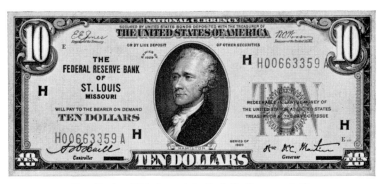

Face Design 410A through L. Back Design on page 30.

410A	Boston	1,680,000	20.00	30.00	42.50
410B	New York	5,556,000	15.00	22.50	30.00
410C	Philadelphia	1,416,000	20.00	32.50	45.00
410D	Cleveland	2,412,000	17.50	25.00	35.00
410E	Richmond	1,356,000	20.00	32.50	45.00
410F	Atlanta	1,056,000	22.50	37.50	50.00
410G	Chicago	3,156,000	15.00	25.00	32.50
410H	St. Louis	1,584,000	20.00	32.50	45.00
410 I	Minneapolis	588,000	27.50	45.00	60.00
410J	Kansas City	1,284,000	22.50	37.50	50.00
410K	Dallas	504,000	30.00	45.00	60.00
410L	San Francisco	1,080,000	22.50	37.50	50.00

$20.00 & $50.00 FEDERAL RESERVE BANK NOTES

420 Twenty Dollars, Portrait of Jackson

Face Design 420A through L. Back Design on page 59.

No.	Federal Reserve Bank	Delivered	Fine	Ex. Fine	New
420A	Boston.....................972,000		$32.50	$45.00	$60.00
420B	New York..............2,568,000		27.50	37.50	50.00
420C	Philadelphia............1,008,000		30.00	40.00	55.00
420D	Cleveland..............1,020,000		30.00	40.00	55.00
420E	Richmond.............1,632,000		28.50	37.50	52.50
420F	Atlanta..................960,000		32.50	45.00	60.00
420G	Chicago................2,028,000		27.50	37.50	50.00
420H	St. Louis................444,000		45.00	67.50	90.00
420 I	Minneapolis.............864,000		30.00	45.00	60.00
420J	Kansas City.............612,000		32.50	45.00	65.00
420K	Dallas...................468,000		40.00	57.50	80.00
420L	San Francisco............888,000		30.00	45.00	60.00

450 Fifty Dollars, Portrait of Grant

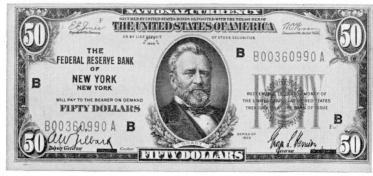

Face Design 450A through L. Back Design on page 66.

$50 & $100 FEDERAL RESERVE BANK NOTES

No.	Federal Reserve Bank	Delivered	Fine	Ex. Fine	New
450A	Boston . . . . No Record		....	....	....
450B	New York 636,000		$70.00	$ 90.00	$125.00
450C	Philadelphia . . . . No Record		....	....	....
450D	Cleveland 684,000		70.00	90.00	125.00
450E	Richmond . . . . No Record		....	....	....
450F	Atlanta . . . . No Record		....	....	....
450G	Chicago 300,000		75.00	100.00	135.00
450H	St. Louis . . . . No Record		....	....	....
450 I	Minneapolis 132,000		90.00	150.00	200.00
450J	Kansas City 276,000		75.00	110.00	140.00
450K	Dallas 168,000		80.00	125.00	175.00
450L	San Francisco 576,000		70.00	90.00	125.00

400   One Hundred Dollars, Portrait of Franklin

Courtesy G. A. Siegwart

Face Design 400A through L. Back Design on page 72.

400A	Boston . . . . No Record		....	....
400B	New York 480,000		125.00	175.00
400C	Philadelphia . . . . No Record		....	....
400D	Cleveland 276,000		150.00	200.00
400E	Richmond 192,000		175.00	225.00
400F	Atlanta . . . . No Record		....	....
400G	Chicago 384,000		125.00	175.00
400H	St. Louis . . . . No Record		....	....
400 I	Minneapolis 144,000		175.00	225.00
400J	Kansas City 96,000		190.00	250.00
400K	Dallas 36,000		200.00	300.00
400L	San Francisco . . . . No Record		....	....

FEDERAL RESERVE NOTES— Green Seal

Federal Reserve Notes were first authorized by the Federal Reserve Act of December 23, 1913. Since then, the issues of these notes have increased to the point that today they comprise about 90% of the total volume of paper money in circulation. Federal Reserve Notes are obligations of the United States and are secured by Gold Certificates or Gold Certificate credits to the amount of at least 25% of the notes in actual circulation. Government securities account for the other 75% of the backing for these notes.

Modern-size Federal Reserve Notes were first issued in 1929, series dated 1928. Denominations range from $1 to $10,000. Those of $500 and higher were discontinued by action of the Board of Governors of the Federal Reserve System on June 26, 1946; however, they will remain in use as long as existing stocks last.

The twelve Federal Reserve Banks are organized and operate for public service as authorized by Congress. They are under supervision of the Board of Governors of the Federal Reserve System, an agency of the Federal Government. Members of this Board are appointed by the President and confirmed by the Senate.

Each of the twelve Banks has nine directors. Three of these, including the Chairman, are appointed by the Board of Governors. The other six are elected by member banks.

When Federal Reserve Notes are finished, they are delivered to the Federal Reserve vault, which is under supervision of the Comptroller of the Currency. They are then sent to the issuing Banks as needed, which in turn distribute them to member banks and to the public.

Federal Reserve Banks release these notes according to the needs of their regions. One can easily tell which Bank issued a particular note by examining its face side. A number and corresponding letter were assigned to each of the Federal Reserve Districts, and both have been used on the notes in various combinations. At present a Bank seal to the left of the portrait carries the letter (and the name of the Bank); this same letter serves as the prefix letter for every serial number on all notes issued by the respective Bank. The District number is imprinted in four places, also on the face of the note. The Treasury seal and serial numbers are in green.

The following notations will clarify various aspects of some issues:

Series of 1928 — The redemption clause on notes issued before 1934 reads as follows: "Redeemable in Gold on Demand at the United States Treasury, or in Gold or Lawful Money at Any Federal Reserve Bank."

Series of 1934 — In 1933, Acts of Congress removed existing legal tender restrictions from all U.S. money, and in 1934 the Gold Reserve Act halted redemption of Federal Reserve Notes with gold. The redemption clause became a legal tender clause in accordance with these Acts, appearing on notes issued from 1934 to 1963 as follows: "This Note is Legal Tender For All Debts, Public and Private, and is Redeemable in Lawful Money at the United States Treasury, or at Any Federal Reserve Bank."

Series of 1934 A — The size of the numerals in the Face Plate Number was made larger on this and succeeding issues.

Series 1950 — The following changes are incorporated on the face side of the notes for this and succeeding issues:

Series designation appears only once, and the word "OF" is deleted.

The Treasury seal and serial numbers are reduced in size.

Signatures are overprinted instead of engraved.

The Bank seal is smaller and has a toothed edge.

$1.00 FEDERAL RESERVE NOTES

Series 1963 — The change in printing method and increase in number of subjects per sheet took place with this issue. Also, this series marks the first appearance of $1 Federal Reserve Notes. The new legal tender clause is the same as that on United States Notes and reads, "This Note is Legal Tender For All Debts, Public and Private." The motto appears on the backs of denominations higher than $1, and the "Will Pay . . ." clause no longer appears on any of the notes.

501 One Dollar, Portrait of Washington

Face Design 501-1A through 1L. Back Design on page 28.

Series 1963   *Signatures:* Granahan-Dillon

No.	Federal Reserve Bank	New
501-1A	Boston	$1.50
501-1B	New York	1.50
501-1C	Philadelphia	1.50
501-1D	Cleveland	1.50
501-1E	Richmond	1.50
501-1F	Atlanta	1.50
501-1G	Chicago	1.50
501-1H	St. Louis	1.50
501-1I	Minneapolis	1.50
501-1J	Kansas City	1.50
501-1K	Dallas	1.50
501-1L	San Francisco	1.50

These notes are frequently sold in sets of twelve, $16.50.

Star notes: Singles, $2.50; sets of twelve, $27.50.

$5.00 FEDERAL RESERVE NOTES

505 Five Dollars, Portrait of Lincoln

Face Design 505-1A through 2L. Back Design on page 23.

Series of 1928   *Signatures:* Tate-Mellon

Large District numeral of Bank at left.

No.	Federal Reserve Bank	V. Fine	Ex. Fine	New
505-1A	Boston...................	$ 8.50	$20.00	$35.00
505-1B	New York................	8.50	20.00	35.00
505-1C	Philadelphia.............	7.00	17.50	32.50
505-1D	Cleveland................	7.00	17.50	35.00
505-1E	Richmond................	10.00	22.50	40.00
505-1F	Atlanta..................	8.50	20.00	37.50
505-1G	Chicago..................	6.50	15.00	27.50
505-1H	St. Louis.................	8.50	20.00	37.50
505-1I	Minneapolis..............	12.50	27.50	50.00
505-1J	Kansas City..............	11.00	25.00	42.50
505-1K	Dallas...................	11.00	25.00	45.00
505-1L	San Francisco............	8.50	20.00	35.00

Series of 1928 A   *Signatures:* Woods-Mellon

Large District numeral at left, similar to Series of 1928 issues.

505-2A	Boston...................	8.00	18.50	30.00
505-2B	New York................	8.00	18.50	30.00
505-2C	Philadelphia.............	6.50	15.00	27.50
505-2D	Cleveland................	6.50	15.00	27.50
505-2E	Richmond................	8.50	20.00	35.00
505-2F	Atlanta..................	8.00	18.50	32.50
505-2G	Chicago..................	6.50	15.00	22.50
505-2H	St. Louis.................	8.00	18.50	32.50
505-2I	Minneapolis..............	11.00	25.00	40.00
505-2J	Kansas City..............	8.50	20.00	37.50
505-2K	Dallas...................	11.00	25.00	40.00
505-2L	San Francisco............	8.00	18.50	30.00

$5.00 FEDERAL RESERVE NOTES

Series of 1928 B   *Signatures:* **Woods-Mellon**

Large District letter replaces numeral in seal on this and succeeding issues.

No.	Federal Reserve Bank	V. Fine	Ex. Fine	New
505-3A	Boston......................	$ 7.00	$ 17.50	$ 27.50
505-3B	New York...................	7.00	17.50	27.50
505-3C	Philadelphia................	6.50	15.00	25.00
505-3D	Cleveland...................	6.50	15.00	25.00
505-3E	Richmond..	10.00	22.50	32.50
505-3F	Atlanta.....................	8.50	20.00	30.00
505-3G	Chicago....................	6.00	12.50	20.00
505-3H	St. Louis...................	8.50	20.00	30.00
505-3I	Minneapolis.................	12.50	27.50	37.50
505-3J	Kansas City................	11.00	25.00	35.00
505-3K	Dallas......................	12.50	27.50	37.50
505-3L	San Francisco...............	7.00	17.50	27.50

Series of 1928 C   *Signatures:* **Woods-Mills**

505-4D	Cleveland...................	25.00	50.00	75.00
505-4F	Atlanta.....................	45.00	90.00	125.00
505-4L	San Francisco...............	35.00	70.00	100.00

Series of 1928 D   *Signatures:* **Woods-Woodin**

505-5F	Atlanta.....................	125.00	175.00	250.00

Quantities issued by each Federal Reserve Bank for each series are not available. Bureau records show totals made for the respective Banks by combining issues of 1928 through 1928 C series, as follows:

Boston................43,056,000
New York.............103,260,000*
Philadelphia............46,560,000
Cleveland..............42,348,000
Richmond..............22,224,000
Atlanta................30,024,000
Chicago...............64,812,000
St. Louis...............28,008,000
Minneapolis............11,436,000
Kansas City............18,036,000
Dallas.................13,752,000
San Francisco..........43,728,000

The Bureau records do not give any indication that any notes were made under Series of 1928 D. Other sources show, however, that the Atlanta Bank did issue the Series of 1928 D note. One is definitely confirmed with serial number F27 881 693A. Other collectors are also requested to submit similar information on this issue.

Valuations for the above notes are based upon their relative scarcity to date.

*This figure is correct according to Mr. Robert H. Lloyd. Bureau records show this total as only 3,260,000 notes, but this resulted from typographical errors. Notes from this issue are known numbered into the 77 millions.

$5.00 FEDERAL RESERVE NOTES

General Face Design 505-3A through 5F. Face Design 505-6AL through 10L.
Back Design on page 23.

Series of 1934 **Signatures:** Julian-Morgenthau

Light Green Seal — Indicated by letter L following
Bank letter in reference number.

No.	Federal Reserve Bank	V. Fine	Ex. Fine	New
505–6AL	Boston......................	$ 6.50	$15.00	$25.00
505–6BL	New York...................	6.00	12.50	22.50
505–6CL	Philadelphia................	6.00	12.50	22.50
505–6DL	Cleveland...................	6.50	15.00	25.00
505–6EL	Richmond...................	11.00	25.00	40.00
505–6FL	Atlanta.....................	20.00	40.00	75.00
505–6GL	Chicago....................	11.00	25.00	40.00
505–6HL	St. Louis...................	15.00	32.50	60.00
505–6IL	Minneapolis.................	11.00	25.00	40.00
505–6JL	Kansas City................	8.50	20.00	30.00
505–6KL	Dallas......................	11.00	25.00	40.00
505–6LL	San Francisco..............	10.00	22.50	35.00

Series of 1934 **Signatures:** Julian-Morgenthau

Dark Green Seal.

No.	Federal Reserve Bank	V. Fine	Ex. Fine	New
505–6A	Boston......................	6.50	15.00	25.00
505–6B	New York...................	6.00	12.50	22.50
505–6C	Philadelphia................	6.00	12.50	22.50
505–6D	Cleveland...................	6.50	15.00	25.00
505–6E	Richmond...................	7.00	17.50	30.00
505–6F	Atlanta.....................	7.00	17.50	30.00
505–6G	Chicago....................	6.00	12.50	22.50
505–6H	St. Louis...................	6.50	15.00	27.50
505–6I	Minneapolis.................	7.00	17.50	32.50
505–6J	Kansas City................	6.50	15.00	27.50
505–6K	Dallas......................	6.50	15.00	27.50
505–6L	San Francisco..............	6.50	15.00	25.00

$5.00 FEDERAL RESERVE NOTES

Series of 1934 A — Signatures: Julian-Morgenthau

No.	Federal Reserve Bank	V. Fine	Ex. Fine	New
505-7A	Boston.....................	$6.00	$12.50	$20.00
505-7B	New York.................	....	10.00	17.50
505-7C	Philadelphia..............	....	10.00	17.50
505-7D	Cleveland.................	6.00	12.50	22.50
505-7E	Richmond.................	6.00	12.50	25.00
505-7F	Atlanta...................	6.00	12.50	25.00
505-7G	Chicago...................	....	10.00	20.00
505-7H	St. Louis.................	6.00	12.50	22.50
505-7L	San Francisco.............	6.00	12.50	22.50

The Bureau of Engraving and Printing records show only the combined totals for series of 1934 and 1934 A issues, as follows:

```
Boston................50,040,000
New York.............173,476,000
Philadelphia...........70,704,000
Cleveland.............57,660,000
Richmond.............66,060,000
Atlanta...............67,776,000
Chicago..............111,736,000
St. Louis.............53,052,000
Minneapolis...........15,468,000
Kansas City...........30,984,000
Dallas................31,560,000
San Francisco.........94,536,000
```

Series of 1934 B — Signatures: Julian-Vinson

No.	Federal Reserve Bank	Delivered	V. Fine	Ex. Fine	New
505-8A	Boston..............	4,548,000	6.50	15.00	27.50
505-8B	New York..........	21,072,000	6.00	12.50	20.00
505-8C	Philadelphia........	9,720,000	6.00	12.50	22.50
505-8D	Cleveland..........	9,816,000	6.00	12.50	22.50
505-8E	Richmond..........	4,968,000	6.50	15.00	27.50
505-8F	Atlanta............	5,280,000	6.50	15.00	27.50
505-8G	Chicago............	10,584,000	6.00	12.50	22.50
505-8H	St. Louis...........	3,120,000	7.00	16.50	30.00
505-8I	Minneapolis.........	2,688,000	7.50	17.50	32.50
505-8J	Kansas City.........	744,000	16.00	30.00	50.00
505-8K	Dallas..........None Printed		....	....	....
505-8L	San Francisco.......	10,108,000	6.00	12.50	22.50

Series of 1934 C — Signatures: Julian-Snyder

No.	Federal Reserve Bank	Delivered	Ex. Fine	New
505-9A	Boston.....................	13,788,000	8.50	15.00
505-9B	New York..................	63,232,000	7.50	12.50
505-9C	Philadelphia...............	21,844,000	8.50	15.00
505-9D	Cleveland.................	20,412,000	8.50	15.00
505-9E	Richmond.................	22,968,000	8.50	15.00

$5.00 FEDERAL RESERVE NOTES

No.	Federal Reserve Bank	Delivered	Ex. Fine	New
505-9F	Atlanta	21,720,000	$ 8.50	$15.00
505-9G	Chicago	57,744,000	7.50	12.50
505-9H	St. Louis	19,824,000	8.50	15.00
505-9I	Minneapolis	4,824,000	10.00	17.50
505-9J	Kansas City	6,384,000	9.50	17.50
505-9K	Dallas	4,776,000	10.00	17.50
505-9L	San Francisco	7,848,000	9.00	17.50

Series of 1934 D   *Signatures:* Clarke-Snyder

No.	Federal Reserve Bank	Delivered	Ex. Fine	New
505-10A	Boston	12,178,000	7.50	12.00
505-10B	New York	54,924,000	7.00	11.00
505-10C	Philadelphia	12,796,000	7.50	12.00
505-10D	Cleveland	10,420,000	7.50	12.50
505-10E	Richmond	13,174,000	7.50	12.00
505-10F	Atlanta	10,036,000	7.50	12.50
505-10G	Chicago	36,576,000	7.00	11.00
505-10H	St. Louis	7,796,000	8.00	13.50
505-10I	Minneapolis	3,648,000	8.50	15.00
505-10J	Kansas City	6,812,000	8.00	13.50
505-10K	Dallas	1,944,000	9.00	17.50
505-10L	San Francisco	11,284,000	7.50	12.00

Face Design 505-11A through 15L. Back Design on page 23.

Series 1950   *Signatures:* Clarke-Snyder

No.	Federal Reserve Bank	Delivered	Ex. Fine	New
505-11A	Boston	30,672,000	6.50	11.00
505-11B	New York	106,768,000	6.00	10.00
505-11C	Philadelphia	44,784,000	6.50	11.00
505-11D	Cleveland	54,000,000	6.50	11.00
505-11E	Richmond	47,088,000	6.50	11.00
505-11F	Atlanta	52,416,000	6.50	11.00

$5.00 FEDERAL RESERVE NOTES

No.	Federal Reserve Bank	Delivered	Ex. Fine	New
505-11G	Chicago.....................85,104,000		$6.00	$10.00
505-11H	St. Louis.....................36,864,000		6.50	11.00
505-11I	Minneapolis.................11,796,000		8.50	13.50
505-11J	Kansas City.................25,428,000		6.50	12.00
505-11K	Dallas.....................22,848,000		6.50	12.00
505-11L	San Francisco................55,008,000		6.00	11.00

Series 1950 A — Signatures: Priest-Humphrey

No.	Federal Reserve Bank	Delivered	Ex. Fine	New
505-12A	Boston.....................53,568,000		6.00	10.00
505-12B	New York...................186,472,000		5.50	9.00
505-12C	Philadelphia.................69,616,000		6.00	10.00
505-12D	Cleveland....................45,360,000		6.00	10.00
505-12E	Richmond...................76,672,000		6.00	10.00
505-12F	Atlanta.....................86,464,000		6.00	10.00
505-12G	Chicago....................129,296,000		5.50	9.00
505-12H	St. Louis.....................54,936,000		6.00	10.00
505-12I	Minneapolis.................11,232,000		7.50	12.50
505-12J	Kansas City.................29,952,000		6.50	11.00
505-12K	Dallas.....................24,984,000		6.50	11.00
505-12L	San Francisco................90,712,000		6.00	10.00

Series 1950 B — Signatures: Priest-Anderson

No.	Federal Reserve Bank	Delivered	Ex. Fine	New
505-13A	Boston.....................30,880,000		7.00	12.50
505-13B	New York...................85,960,000		6.50	10.00
505-13C	Philadelphia.................43,560,000		6.50	11.50
505-13D	Cleveland....................38,800,000		6.50	12.00
505-13E	Richmond...................52,920,000		6.00	11.00
505-13F	Atlanta.....................80,560,000		6.00	11.00
505-13G	Chicago....................104,320,000		6.00	10.00
505-13H	St. Louis.....................25,840,000		7.00	13.50
505-13I	Minneapolis.................20,880,000		7.50	15.00
505-13J	Kansas City.................32,400,000		7.00	12.50
505-13K	Dallas.....................52,119,999		6.00	11.00
505-13L	San Francisco................56,080,000		6.00	11.00

Series 1950 C — Signatures: Smith-Dillon

No.	Federal Reserve Bank	Delivered	Ex. Fine	New
505-14A	Boston.....................20,880,000		6.50	12.50
505-14B	New York...................47,440,000		6.00	10.00
505-14C	Philadelphia.................29,520,000		6.00	11.50

$5.00 FEDERAL RESERVE NOTES

No.	Federal Reserve Bank	Delivered	Ex. Fine	New
505-14D	Cleveland.....................33,840,000		$6.00	$11.00
505-14E	Richmond...................33,480,000		6.00	11.00
505-14F	Atlanta.......................54,360,000		6.00	10.00
505-14G	Chicago......................56,880,000		6.00	10.00
505-14H	St. Louis.....................22,680,000		6.50	12.00
505-14I	Minneapolis.................12,960,000		7.00	12.50
505-14J	Kansas City.................24,760,000		6.00	12.00
505-14K	Dallas..........................3,960,000		8.00	15.00
505-14L	San Francisco................25,920,000		6.00	12.00

Series 1950 D　　　　　　　　　　*Signatures:* Granahan-Dillon

505-15A	Boston...................................Current		8.50
505-15B	New York...............................Current		8.50
505-15C	Philadelphia...........................Current		8.50
505-15D	Cleveland...............................Current		8.50
505-15E	Richmond...............................Current		9.50
505-15F	Atlanta...................................Current		9.50
505-15G	Chicago..................................Current		8.50
505-15H	St. Louis.................................Current		9.50
505-15I	Minneapolis............................Current		9.50
505-15J	Kansas City............................Current		9.50
505-15K	Dallas....................................Current		9.50
505-15L	San Francisco..........................Current		8.50

Series 1963　　　　　　　　　　*Signatures:* Granahan-Dillon

Motto "In God We Trust" added on the back.

505-16A	Boston...................................Current	....
505-16B	New York...............................Current	....
505-16C	Philadelphia...........................Current	....
505-16D	Cleveland...............................Current	....
505-16E	Richmond...............................Current	....
505-16F	Atlanta...................................Current	....
505-16G	Chicago..................................Current	....
505-16H	St. Louis.................................Current	....
505-16I	Minneapolis............................Current	....
505-16J	Kansas City............................Current	....
505-16K	Dallas....................................Current	....
505-16L	San Francisco..........................Current	....

$10.00 FEDERAL RESERVE NOTES

510 Ten Dollars, Portrait of Hamilton

Face Design 510-1A through 2L. Back Design on page 30.

Series of 1928   *Signatures:* Tate-Mellon

Large District numeral of Bank at left.

No.	Federal Reserve Bank	V. Fine	Ex. Fine	New
510-1A	Boston....................	$16.00	$27.50	$37.50
510-1B	New York.................	15.00	25.00	35.00
510-1C	Philadelphia..............	16.00	27.50	37.50
510-1D	Cleveland.................	16.00	27.50	37.50
510-1E	Richmond.................	17.50	30.00	40.00
510-1F	Atlanta...................	17.50	30.00	40.00
510-1G	Chicago...................	12.00	20.00	35.00
510-1H	St. Louis.................	17.50	30.00	40.00
510-1I	Minneapolis...............	17.50	30.00	45.00
510-1J	Kansas City..............	17.50	30.00	45.00
510-1K	Dallas....................	20.00	35.00	50.00
510-1L	San Francisco.............	15.00	25.00	35.00

Series of 1928 A   *Signatures:* Woods-Mellon

Large District numeral at left, similar to Series of 1928 issues.

510-2A	Boston....................	15.00	25.00	32.50
510-2B	New York.................	13.00	22.50	30.00
510-2C	Philadelphia..............	15.00	25.00	32.50
510-2D	Cleveland.................	15.00	25.00	32.50
510-2E	Richmond.................	16.00	27.50	35.00
510-2F	Atlanta...................	16.00	27.50	35.00
510-2G	Chicago...................	13.00	22.50	30.00
510-2H	St. Louis.................	16.00	27.50	35.00
510-2I	Minneapolis...............	17.50	30.00	40.00
510-2J	Kansas City..............	17.50	30.00	40.00
510-2K	Dallas....................	20.00	35.00	45.00
510-2L	San Francisco.............	13.00	22.50	30.00

$10.00 FEDERAL RESERVE NOTES

Series of 1928 B   *Signatures:* **Woods-Mellon**

Large District letter replaces numeral in seal on this and succeeding issues.

No.	Federal Reserve Bank	V. Fine	Ex. Fine	New
510-3A	Boston.....................	$13.00	$22.50	$30.00
510-3B	New York..................	12.00	20.00	27.50
510-3C	Philadelphia...............	13.00	22.50	30.00
510-3D	Cleveland..................	13.00	22.50	30.00
510-3E	Richmond.................	15.00	25.00	32.50
510-3F	Atlanta....................	15.00	25.00	32.50
510-3G	Chicago...................	12.00	20.00	27.50
510-3H	St. Louis..................	15.00	25.00	32.50
510-3I	Minneapolis...............	16.00	27.50	37.50
510-3J	Kansas City...............	16.00	27.50	37.50
510-3K	Dallas.....................	18.00	32.50	42.50
510-3L	San Francisco..............	12.00	20.00	27.50

Series of 1928 C   *Signatures:* **Woods-Mills**

No.	Federal Reserve Bank	V. Fine	Ex. Fine	New
510-4B	New York..................	15.00	25.00	40.00
510-4D	Cleveland..................	15.00	25.00	40.00
510-4E	Richmond.................	17.50	30.00	45.00
510-4F	Atlanta....................	17.50	30.00	45.00
510-4G	Chicago...................	15.00	25.00	40.00

Quantities issued by each Federal Reserve Bank for each series are not available. Bureau records show totals made for the respective Banks by combining issues of 1928 through 1928 C series, as follows:

Boston......................	43,944,000
New York..................	73,944,000
Philadelphia...............	32,520,000
Cleveland..................	32,532,000
Richmond.................	17,604,000
Atlanta....................	15,576,000
Chicago...................	55,104,000
St. Louis..................	15,360,000
Minneapolis...............	9,120,000
Kansas City...............	11,640,000
Dallas.....................	8,712,000
San Francisco.............	23,448,000

Valuations for the above notes are based upon their relative **scarcity to date.**

$10.00 FEDERAL RESERVE NOTES

General Face Design 510-3A through 4G. Face Design 510-5AL through 9L. Back Design on page 30.

Series of 1934   *Signatures:* Julian-Morgenthau

Light Green Seal — Indicated by letter L following
Bank letter in reference number.

No.	Federal Reserve Bank	V. Fine	Ex. Fine	New
510-5AL	Boston	$12.00	$20.00	$27.50
510-5BL	New York	11.00	17.50	25.00
510-5CL	Philadelphia	12.00	20.00	30.00
510-5DL	Cleveland	13.00	22.50	32.50
510-5EL	Richmond	13.00	22.50	32.50
510-5FL	Atlanta	15.00	25.00	35.00
510-5GL	Chicago	11.00	17.50	25.00
510-5HL	St. Louis	15.00	25.00	35.00
510-5IL	Minneapolis	17.50	30.00	40.00
510-5JL	Kansas City	16.00	27.50	37.50
510-5KL	Dallas	16.00	27.50	37.50
510-5LL	San Francisco	12.00	20.00	27.50

Series of 1934   *Signatures:* Julian-Morgenthau

Dark Green Seal.

No.	Federal Reserve Bank	V. Fine	Ex. Fine	New
510-5A	Boston	11.00	17.50	25.00
510-5B	New York	11.00	17.50	25.00
510-5C	Philadelphia	11.00	17.50	27.50
510-5D	Cleveland	12.00	20.00	30.00
510-5E	Richmond	12.00	20.00	32.50
510-5F	Atlanta	13.00	22.50	35.00
510-5G	Chicago	11.00	17.50	25.00
510-5H	St. Louis	12.00	20.00	30.00
510-5I	Minneapolis	13.00	22.50	35.00
510-5J	Kansas City	12.00	20.00	32.50
510-5K	Dallas	12.00	20.00	32.50
510-5L	San Francisco	11.00	17.50	25.00

$10.00 FEDERAL RESERVE NOTES

Series of 1934 A   *Signatures:* **Julian-Morgenthau**

No.	Federal Reserve Bank	V. Fine	Ex. Fine	New
510-6A	Boston.....................	$11.00	$17.50	$25.00
510-6B	New York..................	11.00	17.50	22.50
510-6C	Philadelphia...............	11.00	17.50	25.00
510-6D	Cleveland..................	11.50	18.50	27.50
510-6E	Richmond..................	11.50	18.50	27.50
510-6F	Atlanta....................	11.50	18.50	27.50
510-6G	Chicago....................	11.00	17.50	22.50
510-6H	St. Louis..................	12.00	20.00	30.00
510-6I	Minneapolis................	13.00	22.50	35.00
510-6J	Kansas City...............	12.00	20.00	30.00
510-6K	Dallas.....................	12.00	20.00	32.50
510-6L	San Francisco.............	11.00	17.50	25.00

Quantities issued for the foregoing notes in the 1934 and 1934 A series are only available for each issuing Bank as a whole, as shown in the following table:

Boston....................	138,292,000
New York.................	371,688,000
Philadelphia..............	123,172,000
Cleveland................	No Record*
Richmond................	110,992,000
Atlanta...................	98,652,000
Chicago..................	231,344,000
St. Louis.................	69,528,000
Minneapolis..............	31,392,000
Kansas City..............	50,556,000
Dallas...................	44,688,000
San Francisco............	153,892,000

*Bureau records do not contain a combined total for Cleveland issues of the 1934 and 1934 A series. Instead, the closing serial number is given for issues through *1934 B* as D17 328 000B. Evidently the D—A series of 100,000,000 notes was printed and an additional 17,328,000 were issued with the D—B serial numbers. The total for 1934, 1934 A and 1934 B Cleveland issues thus appears to be 117,328,000 notes. Valuations reflect relative scarcity.

Series of 1934 B   *Signatures:* **Julian-Vinson**

No.	Federal Reserve Bank	Delivered	V. Fine	Ex. Fine	New
510-7A	Boston..............	6,480,000	11.00	17.50	27.50
510-7B	New York..........	42,616,000	....	15.00	20.00
510-7C	Philadelphia........	10,332,000	11.00	17.50	25.00
510-7D	Cleveland..........	No Record	11.00	17.50	25.00
510-7E	Richmond...........	6,912,000	12.00	20.00	27.50
510-7F	Atlanta.............	6,700,000	12.00	20.00	27.50
510-7G	Chicago............	17,664,000	....	15.00	22.50
510-7H	St. Louis...........	5,568,000	12.00	20.00	30.00
510-7I	Minneapolis.........	2,412,000	15.00	25.00	35.00
510-7J	Kansas City.........	4,356,000	13.00	22.50	32.50
510-7K	Dallas..............	5,304,000	13.00	22.50	32.50
510-7L	San Francisco........	9,240,000	11.00	17.50	25.00

$10.00 FEDERAL RESERVE NOTES

Series of 1934 C   *Signatures:* Julian-Snyder

No.	Federal Reserve Bank	Delivered	Ex. Fine	New
510-8A	Boston	43,980,000	$15.00	$22.50
510-8B	New York	108,532,000	12.50	20.00
510-8C	Philadelphia	42,072,000	15.00	22.50
510-8D	Cleveland	43,152,000	15.00	22.50
510-8E	Richmond	34,452,000	15.00	23.50
510-8F	Atlanta	44,372,000	15.00	22.50
510-8G	Chicago	95,456,000	12.50	20.00
510-8H	St. Louis	33,520,000	15.00	25.00
510-8I	Minneapolis	9,936,000	20.00	35.00
510-8J	Kansas City	19,836,000	17.50	30.00
510-8K	Dallas	23,040,000	17.50	30.00
510-8L	San Francisco	41,092,000	15.00	22.50

Series of 1934 D   *Signatures:* Clarke-Snyder

510-9A	Boston	19,972,000	13.50	20.00
510-9B	New York	60,452,000	13.50	18.50
510-9C	Philadelphia	19,184,000	13.50	20.00
510-9D	Cleveland	20,220,000	13.50	20.00
510-9E	Richmond	18,644,000	13.50	20.00
510-9F	Atlanta	17,180,000	13.50	22.50
510-9G	Chicago	55,692,000	13.50	18.50
510-9H	St. Louis	13,796,000	15.00	25.00
510-9I	Minneapolis	5,392,000	17.50	32.50
510-9J	Kansas City	7,992,000	17.50	30.00
510-9K	Dallas	7,680,000	17.50	30.00
510-9L	San Francisco	24,312,000	13.50	20.00

Face Design 510-10A through 14L. Back Design on page 30.

$10.00 FEDERAL RESERVE NOTES

Series 1950   *Signatures:* Clarke-Snyder

No.	Federal Reserve Bank	Delivered	Ex. Fine	New
510-10A	Boston	70,992,000	$12.00	$18.50
510-10B	New York	218,576,000	12.00	15.00
510-10C	Philadelphia	76,320,000	12.00	17.50
510-10D	Cleveland	76,032,000	12.00	17.50
510-10E	Richmond	61,776,000	12.00	18.50
510-10F	Atlanta	63,792,000	12.00	18.50
510-10G	Chicago	161,056,000	12.00	15.00
510-10H	St. Louis	47,808,000	12.00	18.50
510-10I	Minneapolis	18,864,000	12.50	22.50
510-10J	Kansas City	36,332,000	12.00	20.00
510-10K	Dallas	33,264,000	12.00	20.00
510-10L	San Francisco	76,896,000	12.00	17.50

Series 1950 A   *Signatures:* Priest-Humphrey

No.	Federal Reserve Bank	Delivered	Ex. Fine	New
510-11A	Boston	104,248,000	....	15.00
510-11B	New York	356,664,000	....	15.00
510-11C	Philadelphia	73,920,000	11.00	17.50
510-11D	Cleveland	75,088,000	11.00	17.50
510-11E	Richmond	82,144,000	11.00	17.50
510-11F	Atlanta	73,288,000	11.00	17.50
510-11G	Chicago	235,064,000	....	15.00
510-11H	St. Louis	46,512,000	12.00	18.50
510-11I	Minneapolis	8,136,000	15.00	22.50
510-11J	Kansas City	25,488,000	12.00	18.50
510-11K	Dallas	21,816,000	12.50	20.00
510-11L	San Francisco	101,584,000	....	15.00

Series 1950 B   *Signatures:* Priest-Anderson

No.	Federal Reserve Bank	Delivered	Ex. Fine	New
510-12A	Boston	49,240,000	....	15.00
510-12B	New York	170,840,000	....	13.50
510-12C	Philadelphia	66,880,000	....	15.00
510-12D	Cleveland	55,360,000	....	15.00
510-12E	Richmond	51,120,000	....	15.00
510-12F	Atlanta	66,520,000	....	15.00
510-12G	Chicago	165,080,000	....	13.50
510-12H	St. Louis	33,040,000	....	15.00
510-12I	Minneapolis	13,320,000	11.00	17.50
510-12J	Kansas City	34,480,000	....	15.00
510-12K	Dallas	26,280,000	....	15.00
510-12L	San Francisco	55,000,000	....	15.00

Series 1950 C *Signatures:* **Smith-Dillon**

No.	Federal Reserve Bank	Delivered	New
510-13A	Boston	51,120,000	$13.50
510-13B	New York	126,520,000	13.50
510-13C	Philadelphia	25,200,000	14.00
510-13D	Cleveland	33,120,000	14.00
510-13E	Richmond	45,640,000	13.50
510-13F	Atlanta	39,120,000	14.00
510-13G	Chicago	69,400,000	13.50
510-13H	St. Louis	23,040,000	14.50
510-13I	Minneapolis	9,000,000	17.50
510-13J	Kansas City	23,320,000	14.50
510-13K	Dallas	17,640,000	15.00
510-13L	San Francisco	35,640,000	13.50

Series 1950 D *Signatures:* **Granahan-Dillon**

No.	Federal Reserve Bank	Delivered	New
510-14A	Boston	Current	12.50
510-14B	New York	Current	12.50
510-14C	Philadelphia	Current	12.50
510-14D	Cleveland	Current	12.50
510-14E	Richmond	Current	13.50
510-14F	Atlanta	Current	13.50
510-14G	Chicago	Current	12.50
510-14H	St. Louis	Current	13.50
510-14I	Minneapolis	Current	13.50
510-14J	Kansas City	Current	13.50
510-14K	Dallas	Current	13.50
510-14L	San Francisco	Current	12.50

Face Design 510-15A through 15L

$10.00 & $20.00 FEDERAL RESERVE NOTES

Back Design 510-15A through 15L

Series 1963   *Signatures:* **Granahan-Dillon**

Motto "In God We Trust" added on the back.

No.	Federal Reserve Bank	Delivered	New
510–15A	Boston.............................Current	....
510–15B	New York..........................Current	....
510–15C	Philadelphia.......................Current	....
510–15D	Cleveland..........................Current	....
510–15E	Richmond..........................Current	....
510–15F	Atlanta............................Current	....
510–15G	Chicago............................Current	....
510–15H	St. Louis..........................Current	....
510–15I	Minneapolis........................Current	....
510–15J	Kansas City........................Current	....
510–15K	Dallas.............................Current	....
510–15L	San Francisco......................Current	....

$20.00 FEDERAL RESERVE NOTES
520 Twenty Dollars, Portrait of Jackson

Face Design 520-1A through 2L

$20.00 FEDERAL RESERVE NOTES

Back Design 520-1A through 8L; 320; 420; 620.

Series of 1928   *Signatures:* Tate-Mellon

Large District numeral of Bank at left.

No.	Federal Reserve Bank	V. Fine	Ex. Fine	New
520-1A	Boston.....................	$24.00	$32.50	$50.00
520-1B	New York..................	23.00	30.00	45.00
520-1C	Philadelphia...............	24.00	32.50	50.00
520-1D	Cleveland..................	23.00	30.00	45.00
520-1E	Richmond..................	27.50	35.00	55.00
520-1F	Atlanta....................	27.50	35.00	55.00
520-1G	Chicago....................	23.00	30.00	45.00
520-1H	St. Louis..................	27.50	35.00	60.00
520-1I	Minneapolis................	31.50	40.00	65.00
520-1J	Kansas City................	27.50	35.00	60.00
520-1K	Dallas.....................	29.00	37.50	65.00
520-1L	San Francisco..............	24.00	32.50	50.00

Series of 1928 A   *Signatures:* Woods-Mellon

Large District numeral at left, similar to Series of 1928 issues.

No.	Federal Reserve Bank	V. Fine	Ex. Fine	New
520-2A	Boston.....................	24.00	32.50	50.00
520-2B	New York..................	23.00	30.00	42.50
520-2C	Philadelphia...............	24.00	32.50	50.00
520-2D	Cleveland..................	23.00	30.00	45.00
520-2E	Richmond..................	27.50	35.00	55.00
520-2F	Atlanta....................	27.50	35.00	55.00
520-2G	Chicago....................	23.00	30.00	42.50
520-2H	St. Louis..................	27.50	35.00	60.00
520-2I	Minneapolis................		Unknown	
520-2J	Kansas City................	27.50	35.00	65.00
520-2K	Dallas.....................	29.00	37.50	65.00
520-2L	San Francisco..............		Unknown	

$20.00 FEDERAL RESERVE NOTES

Series of 1928 B   *Signatures:* Woods-Mellon

Large District letter replaces numeral in seal on this and succeeding issues.

No.	Federal Reserve Bank	V. Fine	Ex. Fine	New
520-3A	Boston	$23.00	$30.00	$42.50
520-3B	New York	21.00	27.50	40.00
520-3C	Philadelphia	23.00	30.00	42.50
520-3D	Cleveland	23.00	30.00	42.50
520-3E	Richmond	23.00	30.00	45.00
520-3F	Atlanta	23.00	30.00	45.00
520-3G	Chicago	21.00	27.50	40.00
520-3H	St. Louis	24.00	32.50	45.00
520-3I	Minneapolis	24.00	32.50	47.50
520-3J	Kansas City	23.00	30.00	45.00
520-3K	Dallas	27.50	35.00	47.50
520-3L	San Francisco	23.00	30.00	42.50

Series of 1928 C   *Signatures:* Woods-Mills

520-4G	Chicago	35.00	45.00	75.00
520-4L	San Francisco	35.00	45.00	75.00

Bureau records contain quantities issued by each Federal Reserve Bank only in composite totals for notes of the 1928, 1928 A, 1928 B and 1928 C series, as follows:

Boston.....................12,168,000
New York..................31,500,000
Philadelphia...............13,440,000
Cleveland..................22,416,000
Richmond...................9,660,000
Atlanta.....................7,416,000
Chicago....................31,020,000
St. Louis...................6,852,000
Minneapolis................5,844,000
Kansas City................7,440,000
Dallas.....................4,380,000
San Francisco..............17,184,000

Valuations for these notes indicate their relative scarcity to date.

Series of 1934   *Signatures:* Julian-Morgenthau

Light Green Seal — Indicated by letter L following
Bank letter in reference number.

No.	Federal Reserve Bank	Ex. Fine	New
520-5AL	Boston	30.00	42.50
520-5BL	New York	27.50	37.50
520-5CL	Philadelphia	27.50	40.00
520-5DL	Cleveland	27.50	40.00
520-5EL	Richmond	27.50	40.00
520-5FL	Atlanta	30.00	42.50

$20.00 FEDERAL RESERVE NOTES

Face Design 520-3A through 4L. General Face Design 520-5AL through 9L.

No.	Federal Reserve Bank	Ex. Fine	New
520-5GL	Chicago................................	$27.50	$37.50
520-5HL	St. Louis................................	30.00	42.50
520-5IL	Minneapolis...........................	32.50	50.00
520-5JL	Kansas City...........................	30.00	45.00
520-5KL	Dallas.................................	30.00	45.00
520-5LL	San Francisco.........................	27.50	37.50

Series of 1934   *Signatures:* **Julian-Morgenthau**

Dark Green Seal.

520-5A	Boston................................	30.00	42.50
520-5B	New York..............................	27.50	37.50
520-5C	Philadelphia..........................	27.50	40.00
520-5D	Cleveland.............................	27.50	40.00
520-5E	Richmond.............................	27.50	40.00
520-5F	Atlanta...............................	30.00	42.50
520-5G	Chicago...............................	27.50	37.50
520-5H	St. Louis..............................	30.00	42.50
520-5I	Minneapolis...........................	32.50	50.00
520-5J	Kansas City...........................	30.00	45.00
520-5K	Dallas.................................	30.00	45.00
520-5L	San Francisco.........................	27.50	37.50

Series of 1934 A   *Signatures:* **Julian-Morgenthau**

520-6A	Boston................................	28.50	40.00
520-6B	New York..............................	27.50	37.50
520-6C	Philadelphia..........................	27.50	37.50
520-6D	Cleveland.............................	28.50	40.00
520-6E	Richmond.............................	28.50	40.00
520-6F	Atlanta...............................	28.50	40.00

$20.00 FEDERAL RESERVE NOTES

No.	Federal Reserve Bank	Ex. Fine	New
520-6G	Chicago	$27.50	$37.50
520-6H	St. Louis	28.50	40.00
520-6I	Minneapolis	30.00	45.00
520-6J	Kansas City	28.50	42.50
520-6K	Dallas	28.50	42.50
520-6L	San Francisco	27.50	37.50

Quantities issued for the foregoing notes of 1934 and 1934 A series are only available for each issuing Bank as a whole, as shown in the following table:

Boston	38,376,000
New York	113,080,000
Philadelphia	45,168,000
Cleveland	67,164,000
Richmond	72,036,000
Atlanta	44,652,000
Chicago	105,316,000
St. Louis	29,364,000
Minneapolis	16,296,000
Kansas City	28,812,000
Dallas	22,164,000
San Francisco	111,952,000

Valuations for the above notes reflect relative scarcity to date.

Series of 1934 B   *Signatures:* Julian-Vinson

No.	Federal Reserve Bank	Delivered	Ex. Fine	New
520-7A	Boston	3,456,000	30.00	45.00
520-7B	New York	24,900,000	25.00	37.50
520-7C	Philadelphia	5,400,000	30.00	42.50
520-7D	Cleveland	3,960,000	30.00	45.00
520-7E	Richmond	8,994,000	28.50	40.00
520-7F	Atlanta	8,976,000	28.50	40.00
520-7G	Chicago	10,280,000	25.00	38.50
520-7H	St. Louis	5,820,000	30.00	42.50
520-7I	Minneapolis	3,036,000	32.50	47.50
520-7J	Kansas City	4,188,000	30.00	42.50
520-7K	Dallas	2,880,000	35.00	50.00
520-7L	San Francisco	9,720,000	28.50	40.00

A New White House Vignette for Series of 1934 C

On November 10, 1948, Treasury Secretary Snyder announced that the $20.00 note was to bear a new engraving of the White House on the back side. The "new look" was made from a photograph of the South front and grounds after the building was renovated. The design used until this time showed the South front as it appeared in 1929.

Various structural modifications can be seen when the two designs are compared. These include a balcony at the second floor level and four chimneys instead of two. Other differences are also visible. Lettering beneath the building is changed from "White House" to "The White House."

$20.00 FEDERAL RESERVE NOTES

The new White House vignette was first used during the issue of notes Series of 1934 C. Both the old and new back designs can be found with this same series date. Subsequent issues all use the new design.

Back Design 520-8A through 14L

Series of 1934 C   *Signatures:* Julian-Snyder

No.	Federal Reserve Bank	Delivered	Ex. Fine	New
520-8A	Boston	8,202,000	$30.00	$45.00
520-8B	New York	17,880,000	27.50	38.50
520-8C	Philadelphia	11,988,000	28.50	40.00
520-8D	Cleveland	17,256,000	27.50	38.50
520-8E	Richmond	23,638,000	27.50	37.50
520-8F	Atlanta	18,456,000	27.50	38.50
520-8G	Chicago	25,716,000	27.50	37.50
520-8H	St. Louis	13,680,000	28.50	40.00
520-8I	Minneapolis	3,282,000	32.50	47.50
520-8J	Kansas City	8,880,000	30.00	45.00
520-8K	Dallas	9,948,000	30.00	42.50
520-8L	San Francisco	20,088,000	27.50	37.50

Series of 1934 D   *Signatures:* Clarke-Snyder

No.	Federal Reserve Bank	Delivered	Ex. Fine	New
520-9A	Boston	4,352,000	30.00	40.00
520-9B	New York	15,460,000	27.50	37.50
520-9C	Philadelphia	3,888,000	30.00	42.50
520-9D	Cleveland	8,704,000	28.50	38.50
520-9E	Richmond	13,812,000	27.50	37.50
520-9F	Atlanta	7,492,000	30.00	40.00
520-9G	Chicago	12,500,000	27.50	37.50
520-9H	St. Louis	6,200,000	30.00	40.00
520-9I	Minneapolis	2,358,000	32.50	45.00
520-9J	Kansas City	4,108,000	30.00	42.50
520-9K	Dallas	3,612,000	32.50	42.50
520-9L	San Francisco	13,416,000	27.50	37.50

$20.00 FEDERAL RESERVE NOTES

Face Design 520-10A through 14L

Series 1950   *Signatures:* Clarke-Snyder

No.	Federal Reserve Bank	Delivered	Ex. Fine	New
520-10A	Boston	23,184,000	$28.50	$38.50
520-10B	New York	80,064,000	23.50	30.00
520-10C	Philadelphia	29,520,000	27.50	37.50
520-10D	Cleveland	51,120,000	27.50	35.00
520-10E	Richmond	67,536,000	25.00	32.50
520-10F	Atlanta	39,312,000	27.50	37.50
520-10G	Chicago	70,464,000	23.50	30.00
520-10H	St. Louis	27,352,000	28.50	37.50
520-10I	Minneapolis	9,216,000	30.00	40.00
520-10J	Kansas City	22,752,000	30.00	38.50
520-10K	Dallas	22,656,000	30.00	38.50
520-10L	San Francisco	70,272,000	25.00	32.50

Series 1950 A   *Signatures:* Priest-Humphrey

520-11A	Boston	19,656,000	25.00	32.50
520-11B	New York	82,568,000	22.50	27.50
520-11C	Philadelphia	16,560,000	27.50	35.00
520-11D	Cleveland	50,320,000	23.50	28.50
520-11E	Richmond	69,544,000	23.00	28.00
520-11F	Atlanta	27,648,000	23.50	30.00
520-11G	Chicago	73,720,000	22.50	27.50
520-11H	St. Louis	22,680,000	25.00	32.50
520-11I	Minneapolis	5,544,000	28.50	37.50
520-11J	Kansas City	22,968,000	25.00	32.50
520-11K	Dallas	10,728,000	27.50	37.50
520-11L	San Francisco	85,528,000	22.50	27.50

$20.00 FEDERAL RESERVE NOTES

Series 1950 B   Signatures: Priest-Anderson

No.	Federal Reserve Bank	Delivered	Ex. Fine	New
520-12A	Boston................5,040,000		$28.50	$35.00
520-12B	New York................49,960,000		22.50	27.50
520-12C	Philadelphia................7,920,000		27.50	35.00
520-12D	Cleveland................38,240,000		23.50	30.00
520-12E	Richmond................42,120,000		23.50	30.00
520-12F	Atlanta................40,240,000		23.50	30.00
520-12G	Chicago................80,560,000		22.50	27.50
520-12H	St. Louis................19,440,000		27.50	32.50
520-12I	Minneapolis................12,240,000		27.50	32.50
520-12J	Kansas City................28,440,000		27.50	32.50
520-12K	Dallas................11,880,000		27.50	32.50
520-12L	San Francisco................51,040,000		22.50	27.50

Series 1950 C   Signatures: Smith-Dillon

520-13A	Boston................7,200,000		25.00	30.00
520-13B	New York................43,200,000		22.50	27.50
520-13C	Philadelphia................7,560,000		25.00	30.00
520-13D	Cleveland................28,440,000		22.50	27.50
520-13E	Richmond................37,000,000		22.50	27.50
520-13F	Atlanta................19,080,000		23.50	28.50
520-13G	Chicago................29,160,000		22.50	27.50
520-13H	St. Louis................12,960,000		25.00	30.00
520-13I	Minneapolis................6,480,000		27.50	32.50
520-13J	Kansas City................18,360,000		25.00	30.00
520-13K	Dallas................9,000,000		25.00	30.00
520-13L	San Francisco................45,360,000		22.50	27.50

Series 1950 D   Signatures: Granahan-Dillon

No.	Federal Reserve Bank	Delivered	New
520-14A	Boston................Current		27.50
520-14B	New York................Current		27.50
520-14C	Philadelphia................Current		27.50
520-14D	Cleveland................Current		27.50
520-14E	Richmond................Current		27.50
520-14F	Atlanta................Current		27.50
520-14G	Chicago................Current		27.50
520-14H	St. Louis................Current		28.50
520-14I	Minneapolis................Current		....
520-14J	Kansas City................Current		28.50
520-14K	Dallas................Current		28.50
520-14L	San Francisco................Current		27.50

Series 1963   Signatures: Granahan-Dillon

Motto "In God We Trust" added.

520-15A
through   Awaiting Release
520-15L

550 Fifty Dollars, Portrait of Grant

Face Design 550-1A through 1L

Back Design 550-1A through 12L; 350; 450; 650.

Series of 1928   *Signatures:* **Woods-Mellon**

Large District numeral of Bank at left.

No.	Federal Reserve Bank	V. Fine	Ex. Fine	New
550-1A	Boston.....................	$60.00	$ 80.00	$115.00
550-1B	New York..................	....	75.00	100.00
550-1C	Philadelphia...............	....	75.00	100.00
550-1D	Cleveland..................	60.00	80.00	115.00
550-1E	Richmond..................	62.50	85.00	125.00
550-1F	Atlanta....................	65.00	90.00	140.00
550-1G	Chicago....................	....	75.00	100.00
550-1H	St. Louis..................	65.00	90.00	140.00
550-1I	Minneapolis................	70.00	100.00	150.00
550-1J	Kansas City...............	65.00	90.00	140.00
550-1K	Dallas.....................	70.00	100.00	150.00
550-1L	San Francisco.............	62.50	85.00	125.00

$50.00 FEDERAL RESERVE NOTES

Face Design 550-2A through 2L. General Face Design 550-3AL through 7L.

Series of 1928 A   *Signatures:* Woods-Mellon

Large District letter replaces numeral in Bank seal
on this and succeeding issues.

No.	Federal Reserve Bank	V. Fine	Ex. Fine	New
550-2A	Boston......................	....	$ 75.00	$ 90.00
550-2B	New York...................	....	75.00	90.00
550-2C	Philadelphia................	....	75.00	90.00
550-2D	Cleveland...................	....	75.00	100.00
550-2E	Richmond...................	$60.00	80.00	115.00
550-2F	Atlanta.....................	62.50	85.00	135.00
550-2G	Chicago.....................	....	75.00	90.00
550-2H	St. Louis...................	62.50	85.00	135.00
550-2I	Minneapolis.................	70.00	100.00	150.00
550-2J	Kansas City................	62.50	85.00	135.00
550-2K	Dallas......................	65.00	90.00	140.00
550-2L	San Francisco...............	60.00	80.00	115.00

Bureau records contain combined totals Series of 1928 and 1928 A for
each Federal Reserve Bank, as follows:

Boston......................2,160,000
New York....................4,548,000
Philadelphia................3,372,000
Cleveland...................3,192,000
Richmond...................1,800,000
Atlanta.....................1,008,000
Chicago.....................6,360,000
St. Louis...................1,092,000
Minneapolis..................636,000
Kansas City..................996,000
Dallas.......................756,000
San Francisco...............1,512,000

Valuations for the above notes reflect relative scarcity to date.

$50.00 FEDERAL RESERVE NOTES

Series of 1934   *Signatures:* Julian-Morgenthau

Light Green Seal — Indicated by letter **L** following
Bank letter in reference number.

No.	Federal Reserve Bank	Ex. Fine	New
550-3AL	Boston	$70.00	$ 90.00
550-3BL	New York	65.00	80.00
550-3CL	Philadelphia	67.50	85.00
550-3DL	Cleveland	65.00	80.00
550-3EL	Richmond	67.50	85.00
550-3FL	Atlanta	70.00	90.00
550-3GL	Chicago	65.00	80.00
550-3HL	St. Louis	72.50	100.00
550-3IL	Minneapolis	75.00	110.00
550-3JL	Kansas City	72.50	100.00
550-3KL	Dallas	72.50	100.00
550-3LL	San Francisco	67.50	85.00

Series of 1934   *Signatures:* Julian-Morgenthau

Dark Green Seal.

550-3A	Boston	70.00	90.00
550-3B	New York	65.00	80.00
550-3C	Philadelphia	67.50	85.00
550-3D	Cleveland	65.00	80.00
550-3E	Richmond	67.50	85.00
550-3F	Atlanta	70.00	90.00
550-3G	Chicago	65.00	80.00
550-3H	St. Louis	72.50	100.00
550-3I	Minneapolis	75.00	110.00
550-3J	Kansas City	72.50	100.00
550-3K	Dallas	72.50	100.00
550-3L	San Francisco	67.50	85.00

Series of 1934 A   *Signatures:* Julian-Morgenthau

550-4A	Boston	67.50	80.00
550-4B	New York	57.50	72.50
550-4C	Philadelphia	Unknown	
550-4D	Cleveland	60.00	75.00
550-4E	Richmond	60.00	75.00
550-4F	Atlanta	67.50	80.00
550-4G	Chicago	60.00	75.00
550-4H	St. Louis	70.00	85.00
550-4I	Minneapolis	72.50	90.00
550-4J	Kansas City	70.00	85.00
550-4K	Dallas	70.00	85.00
550-4L	San Francisco	60.00	75.00

$50.00 FEDERAL RESERVE NOTES

Quantities issued are only available for the 1934 and 1934 A series for each issuing Bank as a whole, as shown in the following table:

Boston	2,940,000
New York	16,404,000
Philadelphia	5,604,000
Cleveland	9,420,000
Richmond	6,648,000
Atlanta	3,276,000
Chicago	9,132,000
St. Louis	1,740,000
Minneapolis	576,000
Kansas City	1,224,000
Dallas	1,392,000
San Francisco	7,824,000

Valuations for these notes reflect relative scarcity to date.

Series of 1934 B   *Signatures:* Julian-Vinson

No.	Federal Reserve Bank	Delivered	Ex. Fine	New
550-5A	Boston None Printed		....	....
550-5B	New York None Printed		....	....
550-5C	Philadelphia	276,000	$67.50	$ 80.00
550-5D	Cleveland	24,000	80.00	100.00
550-5E	Richmond	120,000	70.00	90.00
550-5F	Atlanta	96,000	75.00	95.00
550-5G	Chicago	12,000	80.00	100.00
550-5H	St. Louis	300,000	65.00	80.00
550-5I	Minneapolis	120,000	70.00	90.00
550-5J	Kansas City	180,000	65.00	85.00
550-5K	Dallas	120,000	70.00	90.00
550-5L	San Francisco	372,000	67.50	80.00

Series of 1934 C   *Signatures:* Julian-Snyder

550-6A	Boston	180,000	75.00	100.00
550-6B	New York	1,668,000	65.00	80.00
550-6C	Philadelphia	1,380,000	65.00	80.00
550-6D	Cleveland	2,740,000	62.50	75.00
550-6E	Richmond	2,280,000	62.50	75.00
550-6F	Atlanta	420,000	72.50	90.00
550-6G	Chicago	408,000	72.50	90.00
550-6H	St. Louis	548,000	67.50	85.00
550-6I	Minneapolis	140,000	75.00	100.00
550-6J	Kansas City	408,000	72.50	90.00
550-6K	Dallas	324,000	72.50	90.00
550-6L	San Francisco None Printed		....	....

Series of 1934 D   *Signatures:* Clarke-Snyder

550-7A	Boston	348,000	65.00	80.00
550-7B	New York	1,176,000	60.00	72.50

$50.00 FEDERAL RESERVE NOTES

No.	Federal Reserve Bank	Delivered	Ex. Fine	New
550-7C	Philadelphia....................744,000		$62.50	$75.00
550-7D	Cleveland..................None Printed		....	....
550-7E	Richmond.......................168,000		72.50	90.00
550-7F	Atlanta.........................228,000		67.50	85.00
550-7G	Chicago.........................636,000		62.50	75.00
550-7H	St. Louis...................None Printed		....	....
550-7I	Minneapolis................None Printed		....	....
550-7J	Kansas City...............None Printed		....	....
550-7K	Dallas..........................148,000		72.50	90.00
550-7L	San Francisco.............None Printed		....	....

Face Design 550-8A through 12L

Series 1950   *Signatures:* Clarke-Snyder

550-8A	Boston........................1,248,000		55.00	70.00
550-8B	New York....................10,236,000		55.00	65.00
550-8C	Philadelphia..................2,352,000		55.00	70.00
550-8D	Cleveland.....................6,180,000		55.00	65.00
550-8E	Richmond.....................5,064,000		55.00	65.00
550-8F	Atlanta.......................1,812,000		55.00	70.00
550-8G	Chicago.......................4,212,000		55.00	65.00
550-8H	St. Louis.......................892,000		60.00	75.00
550-8I	Minneapolis....................384,000		65.00	80.00
550-8J	Kansas City....................696,000		60.00	75.00
550-8K	Dallas........................1,100,000		55.00	70.00
550-8L	San Francisco.................3,996,000		55.00	65.00

Series 1950 A   *Signatures:* Priest-Humphrey

550-9A	Boston..........................720,000		55.00	70.00
550-9B	New York.....................6,480,000		55.00	65.00
550-9C	Philadelphia..................1,728,000		55.00	65.00
550-9D	Cleveland.....................1,872,000		55.00	65.00
550-9E	Richmond.....................2,016,000		55.00	65.00
550-9F	Atlanta.........................288,000		57.50	75.00

$50.00 FEDERAL RESERVE NOTES

No.	Federal Reserve Bank	Delivered	Ex. Fine	New
550-9G	Chicago............................2,016,000		$55.00	$65.00
550-9H	St. Louis.............................576,000		55.00	70.00
550-9I	Minneapolis..................None Printed		....	....
550-9J	Kansas City.........................144,000		60.00	80.00
550-9K	Dallas...............................864,000		55.00	70.00
550-9L	San Francisco.......................576,000		55.00	70.00

Series 1950 B   Signatures: Priest-Anderson

No.	Federal Reserve Bank	Delivered	New
550-10A	Boston...................................864,000		65.00
550-10B	New York.............................8,352,000		60.00
550-10C	Philadelphia..........................2,592,000		60.00
550-10D	Cleveland.............................1,728,000		65.00
550-10E	Richmond.............................1,584,000		65.00
550-10F	Atlanta...........................None Printed		....
550-10G	Chicago...............................4,320,000		60.00
550-10H	St. Louis...............................576,000		70.00
550-10I	Minneapolis......................None Printed		....
550-10J	Kansas City...........................1,008,000		65.00
550-10K	Dallas.................................1,008,000		65.00
550-10L	San Francisco.........................1,872,000		65.00

Series 1950 C   Signatures: Smith-Dillon

No.	Federal Reserve Bank	Delivered	New
550-11A	Boston...................................720,000		65.00
550-11B	New York.............................5,328,000		60.00
550-11C	Philadelphia..........................1,296,000		60.00
550-11D	Cleveland.............................1,296,000		60.00
550-11E	Richmond.............................1,296,000		60.00
550-11F	Atlanta...........................None Printed		....
550-11G	Chicago...............................1,728,000		60.00
550-11H	St. Louis...............................576,000		65.00
550-11I	Minneapolis.............................144,000		70.00
550-11J	Kansas City.............................432,000		65.00
550-11K	Dallas...................................720,000		65.00
550-11L	San Francisco.........................1,152,000		60.00

Series 1950 D   Signatures: Granahan-Dillon

No.	Federal Reserve Bank	Delivered	New
550-12A	Boston.................................Current		60.00
550-12B	New York...............................Current		60.00
550-12C	Philadelphia...........................Current		60.00
550-12D	Cleveland..............................Current		60.00
550-12E	Richmond...............................Current		60.00
550-12F	Atlanta................................Current		60.00
550-12G	Chicago................................Current		60.00
550-12H	St. Louis..............................Current		60.00
550-12I	Minneapolis............................Current		60.00
550-12J	Kansas City............................Current		60.00
550-12K	Dallas.................................Current		60.00
550-12L	San Francisco..........................Current		60.00

$100 FEDERAL RESERVE NOTES

500 One Hundred Dollars, Portrait of Franklin

Face Design 500-1A through 1L

Courtesy John McKnight Brown
Back Design 500-1A through 12L; 300; 400; 600

Series of 1928   *Signatures:* Woods-Mellon

Large District numeral of Bank at left.

No.	Federal Reserve Bank	Ex. Fine	New
500-1A	Boston	$150.00	$190.00
500-1B	New York	145.00	185.00
500-1C	Philadelphia	150.00	190.00
500-1D	Cleveland	150.00	190.00
500-1E	Richmond	165.00	200.00
500-1F	Atlanta	165.00	200.00
500-1G	Chicago	140.00	180.00
500-1H	St. Louis	165.00	200.00
500-1I	Minneapolis	175.00	225.00
500-1J	Kansas City	165.00	200.00
500-1K	Dallas	175.00	225.00
500-1L	San Francisco	150.00	190.00

$100 FEDERAL RESERVE NOTES

Face Design 500-2A through 2L. General Face Design 500-3AL through 7L

Series of 1928 A   *Signatures:* **Woods-Mellon**

Large District letter replaces numeral in Bank seal
on this and succeeding issues.

No.	Federal Reserve Bank	Ex. Fine	New
500-2A	Boston.................................	$150.00	$180.00
500-2B	New York..............................	145.00	175.00
500-2C	Philadelphia..........................	150.00	180.00
500-2D	Cleveland.............................	150.00	180.00
500-2E	Richmond.............................	160.00	190.00
500-2F	Atlanta................................	160.00	190.00
500-2G	Chicago...............................	145.00	175.00
500-2H	St. Louis..............................	160.00	190.00
500-2I	Minneapolis...........................	165.00	210.00
500-2J	Kansas City...........................	160.00	190.00
500-2K	Dallas.................................	165.00	210.00
500-2L	San Francisco.........................	150.00	180.00

Combined totals of notes delivered as shown in the following table are for
Series of 1928 and 1928 A inclusive. More precise data for these issues is not
found in Bureau records.

Boston......................	1,320,000
New York...................	3,528,000
Philadelphia................	1,704,000
Cleveland...................	1,212,000
Richmond...................	828,000
Atlanta......................	612,000
Chicago.....................	4,140,000
St. Louis....................	852,000
Minneapolis.................	516,000
Kansas City.................	780,000
Dallas.......................	420,000
San Francisco...............	1,608,000

Valuations for these notes reflect relative scarcity to date.

$100 FEDERAL RESERVE NOTES

Series of 1934   *Signatures:* Julian-Morgenthau

Light Green Seal — Indicated by letter L following
Bank letter in reference number.

No.	Federal Reserve Bank	Ex. Fine	New
500-3AL	Boston	$145.00	$175.00
500-3BL	New York	135.00	165.00
500-3CL	Philadelphia	145.00	175.00
500-3DL	Cleveland	145.00	175.00
500-3EL	Richmond	145.00	175.00
500-3FL	Atlanta	145.00	175.00
500-3GL	Chicago	140.00	170.00
500-3HL	St. Louis	145.00	175.00
500-3IL	Minneapolis	160.00	185.00
500-3JL	Kansas City	145.00	175.00
500-3KL	Dallas	150.00	180.00
500-3LL	San Francisco	140.00	170.00

Series of 1934   *Signatures:* Julian-Morgenthau

Dark Green Seal.

No.	Federal Reserve Bank	Ex. Fine	New
500-3A	Boston	145.00	175.00
500-3B	New York	135.00	165.00
500-3C	Philadelphia	145.00	175.00
500-3D	Cleveland	145.00	175.00
500-3E	Richmond	145.00	175.00
500-3F	Atlanta	145.00	175.00
500-3G	Chicago	140.00	170.00
500-3H	St. Louis	145.00	175.00
500-3I	Minneapolis	160.00	185.00
500-3J	Kansas City	145.00	175.00
500-3K	Dallas	150.00	180.00
500-3L	San Francisco	140.00	170.00

Series of 1934 A   *Signatures:* Julian-Morgenthau

No.	Federal Reserve Bank	Ex. Fine	New
500-4A	Boston	145.00	175.00
500-4B	New York	135.00	165.00
500-4C	Philadelphia	145.00	175.00
500-4D	Cleveland	145.00	175.00
500-4E	Richmond	145.00	175.00
500-4F	Atlanta	145.00	175.00
500-4G	Chicago	140.00	170.00
500-4H	St. Louis	145.00	175.00
500-4I	Minneapolis	160.00	185.00
500-4J	Kansas City	145.00	175.00
500-4K	Dallas	145.00	180.00
500-4L	San Francisco	140.00	170.00

$100 FEDERAL RESERVE NOTES

Combined totals of notes delivered as shown in the following table are for Series of 1934 and 1934 A inclusive. More precise data for these issues is not found in Bureau records.

Boston......................3,696,000
New York...................18,364,000
Philadelphia.................3,420,000
Cleveland....................3,708,000
Richmond....................4,332,000
Atlanta......................3,492,000
Chicago....................10,188,000
St. Louis....................2,472,000
Minneapolis...................900,000
Kansas City..................2,268,000
Dallas.......................1,608,000
San Francisco................7,236,000

Series of 1934 B   Signatures: Julian-Vinson

No.	Federal Reserve Bank	Delivered	Ex. Fine	New
500-5A	Boston................None Printed		....	....
500-5B	New York..............None Printed		....	....
500-5C	Philadelphia..........None Printed		....	....
500-5D	Cleveland...........................12,000		$165.00	$200.00
500-5E	Richmond..........................240,000		135.00	165.00
500-5F	Atlanta...........................120,000		145.00	175.00
500-5G	Chicago............................12,000		165.00	200.00
500-5H	St. Louis.........................132,000		145.00	175.00
500-5I	Minneapolis.......................120,000		145.00	175.00
500-5J	Kansas City........................12,000		165.00	200.00
500-5K	Dallas.............................40,000		150.00	180.00
500-5L	San Francisco.........None Printed		....	....

Series of 1934 C   Signatures: Julian-Snyder

No.	Federal Reserve Bank	Delivered	Ex. Fine	New
500-6A	Boston................None Printed		....	....
500-6B	New York..............None Printed		....	....
500-6C	Philadelphia..........None Printed		....	....
500-6D	Cleveland.........................240,000		145.00	175.00
500-6E	Richmond........................2,272,000		125.00	155.00
500-6F	Atlanta...........................960,000		135.00	165.00
500-6G	Chicago...........................828,000		130.00	160.00
500-6H	St. Louis.......................1,248,000		130.00	160.00
500-6I	Minneapolis.......................632,000		135.00	165.00
500-6J	Kansas City.......................728,000		135.00	165.00
500-6K	Dallas............................680,000		135.00	165.00
500-6L	San Francisco.....................572,000		135.00	165.00

Series of 1934 D   Signatures: Clarke-Snyder

No.	Federal Reserve Bank	Delivered	Ex. Fine	New
500-7A	Boston................None Printed		....	....
500-7B	New York..............None Printed		....	....
500-7C	Philadelphia......................360,000		140.00	165.00
500-7D	Cleveland.............None Printed		....	....

$100 FEDERAL RESERVE NOTES

No.	Federal Reserve Bank	Delivered	Ex. Fine	New
500-7E	Richmond................None Printed		....	....
500-7F	Atlanta........................320,000		$140.00	$165.00
500-7G	Chicago........................340,000		140.00	165.00
500-7H	St. Louis.......................380,000		140.00	165.00
500-7I	Minneapolis..............None Printed		....	....
500-7J	Kansas City..............None Printed		....	....
500-7K	Dallas.........................152,000		135.00	175.00
500-7L	San Francisco............None Printed		....	....

Face Design 500-8A through 12L

Series 1950   *Signatures:* Clarke-Snyder

500-8A	Boston........................768,000		120.00	150.00
500-8B	New York....................3,908,000		110.00	130.00
500-8C	Philadelphia.................1,332,000		115.00	140.00
500-8D	Cleveland....................1,632,000		115.00	140.00
500-8E	Richmond....................4,076,000		110.00	130.00
500-8F	Atlanta.......................1,824,000		115.00	140.00
500-8G	Chicago.......................4,428,000		110.00	130.00
500-8H	St. Louis......................1,284,000		115.00	140.00
500-8I	Minneapolis....................564,000		120.00	150.00
500-8J	Kansas City....................864,000		120.00	150.00
500-8K	Dallas........................1,216,000		115.00	140.00
500-8L	San Francisco................2,524,000		110.00	135.00

Series 1950 A   *Signatures:* Priest-Humphrey

500-9A	Boston........................1,008,000		115.00	130.00
500-9B	New York....................2,880,000		110.00	125.00
500-9C	Philadelphia...................576,000		120.00	140.00
500-9D	Cleveland.....................288,000		125.00	150.00
500-9E	Richmond....................2,160,000		110.00	125.00
500-9F	Atlanta.........................288,000		125.00	150.00
500-9G	Chicago........................864,000		110.00	135.00
500-9H	St. Louis.......................432,000		120.00	140.00

$100 FEDERAL RESERVE NOTES

No.	Federal Reserve Bank	Delivered	Ex. Fine	New
500-9I	Minneapolis....................144,000		$130.00	$160.00
500-9J	Kansas City.....................288,000		125.00	150.00
500-9K	Dallas..........................432,000		120.00	140.00
500-9L	San Francisco...................720,000		115.00	135.00

Series 1950 B   *Signatures:* Priest-Anderson

No.	Federal Reserve Bank		Ex. Fine	New
500-10A	Boston.........................720,000		115.00	135.00
500-10B	New York.....................6,336,000		110.00	125.00
500-10C	Philadelphia....................720,000		115.00	135.00
500-10D	Cleveland.......................432,000		115.00	140.00
500-10E	Richmond.....................1,008,000		110.00	130.00
500-10F	Atlanta.........................576,000		115.00	140.00
500-10G	Chicago.......................2,592,000		110.00	125.00
500-10H	St. Louis......................1,152,000		110.00	130.00
500-10I	Minneapolis....................288,000		115.00	140.00
500-10J	Kansas City.....................720,000		115.00	135.00
500-10K	Dallas........................1,728,000		110.00	130.00
500-10L	San Francisco.................2,880,000		110.00	125.00

Series 1950 C   *Signatures:* Smith-Dillon

No.	Federal Reserve Bank	Delivered	New
500-11A	Boston.........................864,000		130.00
500-11B	New York.....................2,448,000		120.00
500-11C	Philadelphia....................576,000		130.00
500-11D	Cleveland......................576,000		130.00
500-11E	Richmond.....................1,440,000		125.00
500-11F	Atlanta.......................1,296,000		125.00
500-11G	Chicago.......................1,584,000		125.00
500-11H	St. Louis.......................720,000		130.00
500-11I	Minneapolis....................288,000		140.00
500-11J	Kansas City....................432,000		135.00
500-11K	Dallas.........................720,000		130.00
500-11L	San Francisco.................2,160,000		120.00

Series 1950 D   *Signatures:* Granahan-Dillon

No.	Federal Reserve Bank	Delivered	New
500-12A	Boston.........................Current		120.00
500-12B	New York......................Current		120.00
500-12C	Philadelphia...................Current		120.00
500-12D	Cleveland......................Current		120.00
500-12E	Richmond......................Current		120.00
500-12F	Atlanta........................Current		120.00
500-12G	Chicago........................Current		120.00
500-12H	St. Louis.......................Current		120.00
500-12I	Minneapolis....................Current		120.00
500-12J	Kansas City....................Current		120.00
500-12K	Dallas.........................Current		120.00
500-12L	San Francisco..................Current		120.00

$500 FEDERAL RESERVE NOTES

Illustrations for the following high denomination Federal Reserve Notes were obtained through courtesy of the U. S. Bureau of Engraving. Notes shown are Specimen printings, and bear series date varieties of which no regular issues exist.

5500   Five Hundred Dollars, Portrait of McKinley

General Face Design 5500-1A through 2L. Resembling Face Design 6500.

Back Design 5500-1A through 2L; 6500.

	Series of 1928			*Signatures:* Woods-Mellon	
No.	Bank	Delivered	No.	Bank	Delivered
5500-1A	Boston	84,000	**5500-1G**	Chicago	633,000
5500-1B	New York	340,800	**5500-1H**	St. Louis	92,400
5500-1C	Philadelphia	126,000	**5500-1I**	Minneapolis	44,400
5500-1D	Cleveland	154,320	**5500-1J**	Kansas City	91,800
5500-1E	Richmond	93,600	**5500-1K**	Dallas	71,400
5500-1F	Atlanta	64,200	**5500-1L**	San Francisco	105,000

	Series of 1934			*Signatures:* Julian-Morgenthau	
5500-2A	Boston	58,200	**5500-2G**	Chicago	385,200
5500-2B	New York	526,800	**5500-2H**	St. Louis	70,800
5500-2C	Philadelphia	72,000	**5500-2I**	Minneapolis	25,200
5500-2D	Cleveland	57,600	**5500-2J**	Kansas City	79,200
5500-2E	Richmond	66,000	**5500-2K**	Dallas	54,000
5500-2F	Atlanta	103,200	**5500-2L**	San Francisco	158,400

$1,000 FEDERAL RESERVE NOTES

5-1M One Thousand Dollars, Portrait of Cleveland

General Face Design 5-1M-1A through 3L. Resembling Face Design 6-1M.

Back Design 5-1M-1A through 3L; 6-1M.

Series of 1928			*Signatures:* Woods-Mellon		
No.	**Bank**	**Delivered**	**No.**	**Bank**	**Delivered**
5-1M-1A	Boston	52,800	**5-1M-1G**	Chicago	403,596
5-1M-1B	New York	199,200	**5-1M-1H**	St. Louis	55,200
5-1M-1C	Philadelphia	91,200	**5-1M-1I**	Minneapolis	23,400
5-1M-1D	Cleveland	76,200	**5-1M-1J**	Kansas City	58,200
5-1M-1E	Richmond	55,200	**5-1M-1K**	Dallas	36,600
5-1M-1F	Atlanta	44,400	**5-1M-1L**	San Francisco	62,400

Series of 1934			*Signatures:* Julian-Morgenthau		
5-1M-2A	Boston	36,600	**5-1M-2G**	Chicago	116,400
5-1M-2B	New York	352,800	**5-1M-2H**	St. Louis	22,800
5-1M-2C	Philadelphia	36,000	**5-1M-2I**	Minneapolis	7,200
5-1M-2D	Cleveland	27,000	**5-1M-2J**	Kansas City	27,600
5-1M-2E	Richmond	19,800	**5-1M-2K**	Dallas	36,600
5-1M-2F	Atlanta	44,400	**5-1M-2L**	San Francisco	67,200

$1,000 & $5,000 FEDERAL RESERVE NOTES

Series of 1934 A   *Signatures:* **Julian-Morgenthau**

No.	Bank	Delivered
5-1M-3A	Boston	23,000
5-1M-3B	New York	144,000
5-1M-3C	Philadelphia	60,000
5-1M-3D	Cleveland	24,000
5-1M-3E	Richmond	9,000
5-1M-3F	Atlanta	82,200
5-1M-3G	Chicago	163,200
5-1M-3H	St. Louis	31,200
5-1M-3I	Minneapolis	12,000
5-1M-3J	Kansas City	30,000
5-1M-3K	Dallas	None Printed
5-1M-3L	San Francisco	32,400

$5,000 FEDERAL RESERVE NOTES

5-5M   Five Thousand Dollars, Portrait of Madison

General Face Design 5-5M-1A through 2L. Resembling Face Design 6-5M.

Back Design 5-5M-1A through 2L; 6-5M.

$5,000 & $10,000 FEDERAL RESERVE NOTES

Series of 1928   *Signatures:* Woods-Mellon

No.	Bank	Delivered	No.	Bank	Delivered
5-5M-1A	Boston	960	**5-5M-1G**	Chicago	4,440
5-5M-1B	New York	2,400	**5-5M-1H**	St. Louis	None
5-5M-1C	Philadelphia	None	**5-5M-1I**	Minneapolis	None
5-5M-1D	Cleveland	2,400	**5-5M-1J**	Kansas City	480
5-5M-1E	Richmond	3,192	**5-5M-1K**	Dallas	240
5-5M-1F	Atlanta	1,032	**5-5M-1L**	San Francisco	1,224

Series of 1934   *Signatures:* Julian-Morgenthau

No.	Bank	Delivered	No.	Bank	Delivered
5-5M-2A	Boston	6,000	**5-5M-2G**	Chicago	4,800
5-5M-2B	New York	7,800	**5-5M-2H**	St. Louis	2,400
5-5M-2C	Philadelphia	600	**5-5M-2I**	Minneapolis	None
5-5M-2D	Cleveland	1,200	**5-5M-2J**	Kansas City	1,200
5-5M-2E	Richmond	1,200	**5-5M-2K**	Dallas	1,200
5-5M-2F	Atlanta	1,200	**5-5M-2L**	San Francisco	3,000

$10,000 FEDERAL RESERVE NOTES
5-10M   Ten Thousand Dollars, Portrait of Chase

General Face Design 5-10M-1A through 2L. Resembling Face Design 6-10M.

Back Design 5-10M-1A through 2L; 6-10M.

$10,000 FEDERAL RESERVE NOTES

Series of 1928   *Signatures:* Woods-Mellon

No.	Bank	Delivered	No.	Bank	Delivered
5-10M-1A	Boston	960	**5-10M-1G**	Chicago	2,400
5-10M-1B	New York	2,400	**5-10M-1H**	St. Louis	None
5-10M-1C	Philadelphia	None	**5-10M-1I**	Minneapolis	None
5-10M-1D	Cleveland	600	**5-10M-1J**	Kansas City	240
5-10M-1E	Richmond	1,992	**5-10M-1K**	Dallas	240
5-10M-1F	Atlanta	1,032	**5-10M-1L**	San Francisco	1,224

Series of 1934   *Signatures:* Julian-Morgenthau

No.	Bank	Delivered	No.	Bank	Delivered
5-10M-2A	Boston	3,600	**5-10M-2G**	Chicago	3,600
5-10M-2B	New York	7,800	**5-10M-2H**	St. Louis	1,200
5-10M-2C	Philadelphia	600	**5-10M-2I**	Minneapolis	None
5-10M-2D	Cleveland	None	**5-10M-2J**	Kansas City	None
5-10M-2E	Richmond	None	**5-10M-2K**	Dallas	None
5-10M-2F	Atlanta	None	**5-10M-2L**	San Francisco	1,800

———◆—◆———

GOLD CERTIFICATES — Gold Seal

Gold Certificates were not made for general circulation until 1882, though they first appeared in 1865. The first three issues were used for larger commercial transactions and were held mainly by banks and clearing houses. Denominations of large-size notes ranged from $10 to $10,000. These notes were often referred to as "gold backs" because of the orange or gold color found on their backs.

Modern-size Gold Certificates were issued for general circulation from 1929 to 1933, series dated 1928 and 1928 A. Only a small number of the latter were made and issued, as the Emergency Bank Act of 1933 prevented further use of any Gold Certificates and required that they be turned in and exchanged for other currency. On December 28 of that year, Treasury Secretary Morgenthau issued an order prohibiting the holding of these notes by any private individual for any reason. Very few modern-size Gold notes were thus saved, especially in New condition; if any could have been hidden, they would most likely have been the large-size pieces which were naturally included in Morgenthau's order.

The Gold Reserve Act of January 31, 1934 immediately followed; this Act raised the value of gold from $20.67 to $35 per troy ounce, prohibited the circulation of gold coins, and allowed Gold Certificates to be issued only to Federal Reserve Banks. A new series of Gold Certificates, Series of 1934, was made and released to the Federal Reserve Banks in exchange for gold coin or bullion. No specimen of any notes of this series was released outside the Federal Reserve System. The $100,000 note, the highest denomination printed, is included in the Series of 1934 issue.

On April 24, 1964, Treasury Secretary Dillon signed an order removing all restrictions from the holding or acquiring of Gold Certificates issued before passage of the Gold Reserve Act of 1934. This action made possible the entry of these notes into the numismatic market, and they can now be openly collected and exhibited.

Modern-size Gold Certificates Series of 1928 and 1928 A are "Gold Coin" notes, so stated on the face. No heading is found in the usual place at the top; instead, it is to the left of the portrait near the Treasury seal. The color of the seal and serial numbers is gold.

$10.00 & $20.00 GOLD CERTIFICATES

The following notations will further clarify certain aspects of these issues:

Series of 1928 — Notes of this series and the Series of 1928 A carry the following legal tender clause: "This Certificate Is A Legal Tender in the Amount Thereof in Payment of All Debts and Dues Public and Private."

The backs of these notes are all uniform with other modern types of similar denominations, and are printed in green.

Series of 1934 — No notes of this series were released to circulation; therefore, they are not included in the catalog listings. The $100,000 note is illustrated, however, on page 85.

The backs of notes in this series are printed in gold, a radical departure from the green backs of all other types and series of modern notes. The "Gold Coin" clause is not used for this series, but the legal tender clause is the same as on earlier issues except for the deletion of the word "A."

610 Ten Dollars, Portrait of Hamilton

Face Design 610-1 and 2. Back Design on page 30.

No.	Series	Treasurer-Secretary	Delivered	Fine	V. Fine	Ex. Fine	New
610-1	1928	Woods-Mellon	130,812,000	$20.00	$40.00	$ 65.00	$ 85.00
610-2*	1928 A	Woods-Mills	2,544,000	45.00	75.00	175.00	250.00

*This note may not have been issued.

620 Twenty Dollars, Portrait of Jackson

Face Design 620-1 and 2. Back Design on page 59.

$20, $50, $100, $500 & $1,000 GOLD CERTIFICATES

No.	Series	Treasurer-Secretary	Delivered	Fine	V. Fine	Ex. Fine	New
620-1	1928	Woods-Mellon........66,204,000		$ 35.00	$ 65.00	$100.00	$150.00
620-2*	1928 A	Woods-Mills...........1,500,000		75.00	125.00	200.00	300.00

*This note may not have been issued.

650 Fifty Dollars, Portrait of Grant

Face Design 650. Back Design on page 66.

650	1928	Woods-Mellon.........5,520,000		75.00	125.00	225.00	300.00

600 One Hundred Dollars, Portrait of Franklin

Face Design 600. Back Design on page 72.

600	1928	Woods-Mellon.........3,240,000		125.00	150.00	350.00	500.00

6500 Five Hundred Dollars, Portrait of McKinley

See page 78 for Resembling Face and Back Designs.

No.	Series	Treasurer-Secretary	Delivered
6500	1928	Woods-Mellon...........420,000	

6-1M One Thousand Dollars, Portrait of Cleveland

See page 79 for Resembling Face and Back Designs.

6-1M	1928	Woods-Mellon...........288,000	

$5,000, $10,000 & $100,000 GOLD CERTIFICATES

6-5M   Five Thousand Dollars, Portrait of Madison

See page 80 for Resembling Face and Back Designs.

No.	Series	Treasurer-Secretary	Delivered
6-5M	1928	Woods-Mellon 24,000	

6-10M   Ten Thousand Dollars, Portrait of Chase

See page 81 for Resembling Face and Back Designs.

6-10M	1928	Woods-Mellon 48,000	

Gold Certificates were made in the Series of 1934 for use within the Federal Reserve System, and were not allowed into outside circulation. Denominations were $100, $1000, $10,000 and $100,000. This last is the highest denomination of modern-size currency ever printed by the United States, and is shown below. The portrait is of Woodrow Wilson.

The $100,000 Gold Certificate, Series of 1934.

The order of April 24, 1964 legalizing the holding of Gold Certificates covered all such Certificates released to general circulation through January 30, 1934. Thus, no Gold Certificates Series of 1934 may be legally held, since they were all made and delivered after the January 30 cut-off date. For this reason, no Series of 1934 Gold Certificates are numbered in the listings, but their delivery totals are included in Appendix B.

WORLD WAR II ISSUES

The HAWAII Overprints — Brown Seal

These notes were overprinted HAWAII face and back as illustrated. Also, they were prepared with brown seals and serial numbers. These precautionary measures were taken so that in the event of an invasion of Hawaii and the capture of U. S. currency by enemy forces, notes with such colors and markings could have been declared valueless.

All HAWAII overprinted notes bear the signature combination of Julian-Morgenthau. The One Dollar notes are Silver Certificates; $5, $10 and $20 notes are Federal Reserve Notes from the 12th District (San Francisco).

Face Design H201

Back Design H505-1 and 2

No.	Denomination	Series	Delivered	V. Fine	Ex. Fine	New
H201	$ 1.00	1935 A..........35,052,000	$ 3.50	$ 5.00	$ 8.00
H505-1	5.00	1934.............3,000,000	50.00	75.00	100.00
H505-2	5.00	1934 A...........6,416,000	12.50	20.00	35.00
H510	10.00	1934 A..........10,424,000	17.50	27.50	37.50
H520-1	20.00	1934.......included below	150.00	225.00	300.00
H520-2	20.00	1934 A..........11,246,000	30.00	45.00	60.00

WORLD WAR II ISSUES

Back Design H510

Face Design H520-1 and 2

The Yellow Seal North Africa Silver Certificates

These were prepared for use in North Africa. All bear the Julian-Morgenthau signature combination. Though the Treasury seals were printed in yellow, the serial numbers retained their usual blue color.

No.	Denomination	Series	Delivered	V. Fine	Ex. Fine	New
A201	$ 1.00	1935 A.........26,916,000	$ 4.50	$ 6.50	$ 10.00
A205-1*	5.00	1934.......included below	....	....	....
A205-2	5.00	1934 A.........16,660,000	12.50	20.00	27.50
A210-1	10.00	1934.......included below	150.00	225.00	300.00
A210-2	10.00	1934 A.........21,860,000	17.50	25.00	35.00

*This note is believed to exist. It is listed here without any valuation, as there is no known record of sale. Verification of its existence is welcomed.

Bureau records contain only the combined totals for the $5 and $10 notes Series of 1934 and 1934 A, as shown above.

WORLD WAR II ISSUES

Experimental "R" and "S" $1.00 Silver Certificates

These notes were made to test the wearing qualities of regular and special paper. Equal quantities were overprinted on the face with a red R or S, in the position shown. All bear signatures of Julian-Morgenthau and are dated Series 1935 A.

Face Design R201

Face Design S201

No.	Delivered	V. Fine	Ex. Fine	New
R201, with Red R	1,184,000	$25.00	$37.50	$45.00
S201, with Red S	1,184,000	22.50	32.50	40.00

The R and S overprints were made to determine whether a special kind of paper might wear better in circulation than the regular paper normally used. The "R" represented those notes made of regular paper and the "S" was for those notes made of the special paper. Results of the experiment were inconclusive and no change was made in the kind of paper used for U. S. currency.

It is advisable to check the serial numbers given on page 155 in the Appendix when purchasing these notes, as dangerous imitations exist.

UNCUT SHEETS OF CURRENCY
Subjects Per Sheet and Check Letters

Modern U. S. currency has been printed in sheets of 12, 18 and 32 notes. All issues up to April of 1953 were made in 12-subject sheets, with Check Letters from A to L (12 letters for 12 notes). Each note carries two identical Check Letters, which serve to indicate its particular position on the sheet when it was printed. These small capital letters are found in the upper left and lower right areas on the face side. The little number accompanying the lower right Check Letter is the Face Plate Number; it has nothing to do with the sheet position of the note.

On April 2, 1953, the Treasury issued the first notes printed in 18-subject sheets. These carry Check Letters from A through R but are otherwise similar to earlier issues.

On July 25, 1957, the Bureau of Engraving began production of notes printed in sheets of 32 subjects. Each sheet consists of four quadrants of eight notes, as shown in the diagram on page 96. The upper left quadrant contains Check Letters and numbers A1 through H1, the lower left A2 through H2, the upper right A3 through H3 and the lower right A4 through H4. The letter indicates position and the number indicates the quadrant. As with earlier issues, each note bears two identical Check Letters, but there is an important difference. The quadrant number (1 to 4) appears only with the *upper left* Check Letter. The number found with the lower right Check Letter is the Face Plate Number; while it may correspond at times with the quadrant number, it has no relationship to the position or quadrant of the note. (Backs also carry a Back Plate Number; its position varies with the design or denomination.)

Serial Numbering for Different Sizes of Sheets

As the number of subjects per sheet was changed, so also was the system used for placing serial numbers on the notes. The following table shows which system was used for each size of sheet, and applies to all issues except except National Currency Series of 1929 and Federal Reserve Bank Notes:

Size of Sheet	Check Letters	System of Numbering
12 Subjects	A through L	Consecutive numbering by half sheet, six down on the left and six down on the right.
18 Subjects	A through R	Numbering advances by 8,000, six down on the left, six following in the middle and six down on the right.
32 Subjects	A1–H1 A2–H2 A3–H3 A4–H4	Numbering advances by 2,000, proceeding by quadrant from the upper left to the lower right.†

Clarification of 12-Subject Numbering

12-subject sheets exist both with consecutive serial numbers by half sheet as described above and with *all twelve* notes in full consecutive order. An example of each is illustrated on pages 90-91. As explained by the Bureau, the general rule was that sheets intended for processing as regular issues for circulation were numbered by the half sheet according to the following example: Suppose that the total of a particular run was to be 1,200 notes, or 100 sheets.

†This is believed to be correct up to this point. The Bureau of Engraving will not make public any specific data on the numbering of 32-subject sheets, as this is considered to be classified information.

UNCUT SHEETS OF CURRENCY

12-subject sheet of currency with all notes consecutively numbered.

The first sheet would contain serial numbers from 1 to 6 on the left side and 601 to 606 on the right side, the second sheet would have numbers 7 to 12 and 607 to 612, and so on until the end of the run.

Sheets delivered to the Treasurer in uncut form, presumably for release upon request to collectors and others, often but not always bore consecutive numbers for all the notes on the sheet. In 1950, it was officially ordered that all uncut 12-subject sheets scheduled for delivery to the Treasurer should thenceforth bear serial numbers in fully consecutive order for the entire sheet.

UNCUT SHEETS OF CURRENCY

12-subject sheet of currency with notes consecutively numbered by half-sheet, and a number gap between notes in the lower left and upper right positions.

UNCUT SHEETS OF CURRENCY

*AT LEFT: Type One National Currency sheet of six subjects.
Each note has the same serial numbers except for prefix letter.*

*AT RIGHT: Type Two National Currency sheet of six notes.
Serial numbers are consecutive and without suffix letter.*

(For explanation of the above, see pages 32 and 93.)

UNCUT SHEETS OF CURRENCY
Reconstructed Sheets

If a collector is able to locate all of the single notes originally printed as one unit or sheet, he will then be able to show them in the positions they formerly occupied before being cut apart. This group of notes comprises what is termed a "reconstructed sheet" of currency.

Reconstructed half-sheets of 12-subject printings could easily be assembled by obtaining six consecutively numbered notes from a new pack, making sure that Check Letters ran from A to F, or G to L. It would be extremely difficult to assemble all notes for a full 12-subject sheet as evidenced by the explanation of the numbering system on pages 89-90. Reconstruction of larger sheets is practically impossible, since the changes in the numbering system make a difference of 136,000 numbers on each 18-subject sheet and presumably 62,000 numbers on each 32-subject sheet.

Consecutively numbered notes from the 18 or 32-subject sheets are readily available, but are of little consequence since *each note* comes from a *different sheet*. Easy proof of this fact can be seen on the notes themselves; they will all have the same Check Letters indicating identical positions on their respective sheets.

National Currency and Federal Reserve Bank Notes

National Currency and Federal Reserve Bank Notes were printed in sheets of 12 subjects, then cut and delivered in vertical sheets of six subjects.

Type One National Currency used the same serial number and suffix letter for all six notes; however, each note had a different prefix letter (A through F) which also served to denote its position on that particular six-subject sheet.

Type Two National Currency notes were consecutively numbered and bore the same prefix letter, but the suffix letter was dropped. The only way to tell the sheet position of a Type Two note or a Federal Reserve Bank Note is by its Check Letters. (See illustrations of National Currency sheets on opposite page.)

Since National Currency and Federal Reserve Bank Notes were all printed in 12-subject sheets (even though delivered in six-subject sheets), Check Letters proceeded from A to L as on all other 12-subject printings. Thus, it is always possible to pinpoint the exact position of any note on the original 12-subject sheet. Check Letters A through F indicate the left strip of six notes, and G through L indicate the right strip of six notes.

Each note also carries a Face Plate Number in its normal position alongside the lower right Check Letter.

Numbering for Federal Reserve Bank Notes was also consecutive. Every serial number was preceded by the District letter as a prefix, and "A" as a suffix. No single issue was large enough to require the change of suffix letter to "B."

VALUATIONS OF UNCUT SHEETS

The most readily available uncut sheets of any U. S. currency are the six-subject sheets of National Currency which were delivered to issuing banks intact. It is easy to see why quantities of these sheets exist; the banks released the notes as they were needed, and many never used all that they had ordered. Also, quantities of sheets with low serial numbers were preserved for various reasons.

The following valuations apply to any sheet of these notes after the particular rarity rating of the issue as single notes has been ascertained from the listing on page 33.

UNCUT SHEETS OF CURRENCY

18-subject sheet of currency. Numbering advances by 8,000
(see pages 89 and 93 for explanation).

UNCUT SHEETS OF CURRENCY

National Currency Series of 1929

Six-subject Sheets

Denom- ination	Rarity 1 & 2	Rarity 3 & 4	Rarity 5	Rarity 6	Rarity 7	Rarity 8	Rarity 9
$ 5.00	$190.00	$ 225.00	$ 250.00	$ 275.00	$ 350.00	$ 650.00	$900.00
10.00	225.00	250.00	275.00	300.00	400.00	650.00	900.00
20.00	275.00	300.00	325.00	350.00	450.00	750.00	950.00
50.00	650.00	750.00	800.00	850.00	900.00	1000.00	———
100.00	900.00	1000.00	1100.00	1250.00	1500.00	1750.00	———

Until about 1954, it was possible to obtain uncut sheets of currency from the Bureau of Engraving for numismatic and educational purposes. Most sheets released in this manner were of 12 subjects, since the Bureau had only begun the printing of 18-subject sheets during 1953. Shortly thereafter, no more uncut sheets were made available to anyone.

Apparently the two types released in sheets were United States Notes and Silver Certificates. Other types are not presently known to exist.*

All uncut sheets are considered to be in New condition, even though the edges, corners or margins may have minor flaws. The following listing represents all sheets known and occasionally available:

*One six-subject sheet of $10 New York Federal Reserve Bank Notes is recorded in the Grinnell Collection, and is so far the only known sheet of this type of note.

UNITED STATES NOTES

One Dollar

No.	Series	Sheet Size	Valuation
101-1	1928	12 Subjects	$3000.00

Two Dollars

No.	Series	Sheet Size	Valuation
102-1	1928	12 Subjects	550.00
102-2	1928 A	12 Subjects	750.00
102-3	1928 B	12 Subjects	2250.00
102-4	1928 C	12 Subjects	450.00
102-5	1928 D	12 Subjects	400.00
102-6	1928 E	12 Subjects	550.00
102-7	1928 F	12 Subjects	375.00
102-8	1928 G	12 Subjects	350.00
102-9	1953	18 Subjects	650.00

Five Dollars

No.	Series	Sheet Size	Valuation
105-1	1928	12 Subjects	600.00
105-2	1928 A	12 Subjects	850.00
105-3	1928 B	12 Subjects	525.00
105-4	1928 C	12 Subjects	500.00
105-5	1928 D	12 Subjects	750.00
105-6	1928 E	12 Subjects	475.00
105-7	1928 F	12 Subjects	450.00
105-8	1953	18 Subjects	650.00

UNCUT SHEETS OF CURRENCY

E	E3	A	A3	E	E1	A	A1
F	F3	B	B3	F	F1	B	B1
G	G3	C	C3	G	G1	C	C1
H	H3	D	D3	H	H1	D	D1
E	E4	A	A4	E	E2	A	A2
F	F4	B	B4	F	F2	B	B2
G	G4	C	C4	G	G2	C	C2
H	H4	D	D4	H	H2	D	D2

Layout of 32-Subject Currency Sheet

Check letters and quadrant number are shown for each note.

UNCUT SHEETS OF CURRENCY
SILVER CERTIFICATES
One Dollar

No.	Series	Sheet Size	Valuation
201-1	1928	12 Subjects	$ 475.00
201-2	1928 A	12 Subjects	400.00
201-3	1928 B	12 Subjects	425.00
201-4	1928 C	12 Subjects	2250.00
201-5	1928 D	12 Subjects	1750.00
201-6	1928 E	12 Subjects	4250.00
201-7	1934	12 Subjects	400.00
201-8	1935	12 Subjects	450.00
201-9	1935 A	12 Subjects	400.00
201-10	1935 B	12 Subjects	450.00
201-11	1935 C	12 Subjects	400.00
201-12	1935 D	12 Subjects	400.00
201-12	1935 D	18 Subjects	500.00
201-13	1935 E	18 Subjects	475.00

Five Dollars

No.	Series	Sheet Size	Valuation
205-1	1934	12 Subjects	1250.00
205-2	1934 A	12 Subjects	700.00
205-3	1934 B	12 Subjects	850.00
205-4	1934 C	12 Subjects	550.00
205-5	1934 D	12 Subjects	525.00
205-6	1953	18 Subjects	850.00

Ten Dollars

No.	Series	Sheet Size	Valuation
210-1	1933	12 Subjects	Very Rare
210-2	1934	12 Subjects	1000.00
210-3	1934 A	12 Subjects	750.00
210-4	1934 B	12 Subjects	Very Rare
210-5	1934 C	12 Subjects	650.00
210-6	1934 D	12 Subjects	525.00
210-7	1953	18 Subjects	1100.00

WORLD WAR II ISSUES
One Dollar, HAWAII Overprint

H201	1935 A	12 Subjects	850.00

One Dollar, Yellow Seal North Africa

A201	1935 A	12 Subjects	1000.00

APPENDIX A

HISTORY
OF THE
PROPOSAL TO ADOPT THE PHILIPPINE SIZE
OF PAPER CURRENCY FOR USE IN THE
UNITED STATES, AS REVEALED IN
TREASURY RECORDS

Prepared by the
United States Bureau of Efficiency
October 17, 1925

Early Reports and Statements on Currency Size
Made by Secretary MacVeagh in 1910

The MacVeagh committee on design and size of currency, working through 1909-1910, consisting of the Chief of the Division of Loans and Currency, the Treasurer of the United States, the Chief of the Secret Service, and the Director of the Bureau of Engraving and Printing, made a very careful and exhaustive study of the proposal to change the size of the paper currency. It arrived at the following conclusion set down in an undated report: The committee "strongly" recommended adopting the Philippine size which, it said, had proven an unqualified success. It enumerated as savings (1) the additional bills per plate; (2) decrease in piece rate of plate printing; (3) increased production; (4) saving in cost of paper; (5) saving in transportation of paper; (6) reduction in paper handling force; (7) reduction of force in redemption division. It figured the saving on the basis of money output at that time at $612,603 a year.

The committee believed the change in size would be advantageous to banks and commercial houses. The fact that the smaller bills would be carried flat, it held, would make them generally easier to handle. They would occupy less storage space. They would cramp the hand of counters less than the present money. The committee did not believe that the smaller notes would necessitate a change in tills. It did not believe that the temporary inconvenience of changing size would be so serious as to have great weight.

On September 10, 1910, Mr. MacVeagh gave out an interview on the proposed change in design and size of paper money which crystallized his views on the matter. It is important since the file which shows the detail of this investigation has been lost and these general conclusions are its chief record. The following quotation bears on the question of size. Mr. MacVeagh said:

"I am hopeful that the public will consider favorably, as the Treasury Department is inclined to consider favorably, the economies and other advantages which would result ultimately from the use of a somewhat smaller paper currency. It has been suggested that our notes be reduced to $2\frac{1}{2}$ inches wide by 6 inches long, the same size as the Philippine paper currency, which has proved an unqualified success — and a size which, when it is not brought into direct comparison with the present note, and when not scrutinized, would not, to most people, present a noticeable change. From the Treasury point of view, the proposed reduction would result in an estimated saving to the Government of $612,603 every year. This economy would be gained from various sources. For example, we would print five notes where we print four now, and the increased production of 25 per cent more notes with the same labor as at present, carried through all the various processes of wetting, examining, counting, drying, numbering, sealing, separating, etc., would save more than $200,000 a year alone. The saving in the cost of paper would be almost $90,000, and the decrease in the cost of plate printing would amount to almost $270,000. These, with a possible reduction of the force in the redemption division of the Treasurer's office, due to the smaller number of notes redeemed because of the longer life of the smaller notes, represent the chief items in this estimate of $612,000.

"On the popular side, I am inclined to think the change would cause little if any inconvenience and would quickly be commended by the people. The smaller notes could be carried flat and, being preserved in that shape, would not wear from folding and would be more readily handled by cashiers, tellers, and clerks. We have carefully experimented with bank clerks and tellers in the city of Washington and learn that the smaller notes do not tend to cramp the hands of persons manipulating them, as do the present notes, and that they are just as easily handled and counted as the old notes. The smaller notes could be more closely packed on the counters of the banks and, in fact, banks as well as subtreasuries probably could store 25 per cent more of the new than of the old notes in their vaults.

"It will not be necessary to change the dimensions of cash drawers, tills, compartments, etc., which now hold the present size of money as they will hold also currency of the size proposed. This would not be true, of course, if the suggestions were to enlarge the size of the notes.

"The only objection to adopting smaller notes which seems to me of special importance is that for some time two sizes of paper money would be in use and bank tellers and the business public would be correspondingly inconvenienced. I think, however, that this objection could be largely if not almost wholly overcome by preparing in advance enough of the new notes so that they could be exchanged for old notes on a fixed date at all subtreasuries, banks, and other large financial institutions. Preparation for the change, including the making of designs and plates and the printing of notes, probably would require about eighteen months, and within that time, no doubt, enough new notes could be printed to make possible an almost complete change. The people themselves would aid this change naturally and rapidly in their desire to secure specimens of the new money. I am convinced that the criticisms of the proposed issue are based rather upon considerations of temporary inconvenience than upon essential and insurmountable objections. If this is the case, these objections should hardly be permitted to stand in the way of permanent progress and economy.

"No special legislation is necessary to enable the Government to reduce the size of United States notes and gold and silver certificates. In order, however, to effect a reduction in the size of national-bank currency without legislation, and at the same time continue the present multiplicity of designs, it would be necessary to eliminate the 13,000 plates now in use and to engrave as many more. This could be done, I presume, only by the Government's assumption of the expense of new plates, and as each plate costs $75, the total cost of the new series would reach about $900,000. It would be quite possible, however, to use the same uniform engraved plates for all bank notes, and to print later by separate process the name of the individual bank upon the notes which that bank was to issue."

MacVeagh's Official Order of 1913 to Reduce the Size of U. S. Currency

On February 26, 1913, Secretary MacVeagh issued instructions to the Bureau of Engraving and Printing embodying the recommendations of the committee and directing complete redesign of the currency and the adoption of the smaller size. With relation to the question of size the instructions read:

"Confirming my oral approval and instructions of January 31, 1913, the design prepared by Mr. Kenyon Cox, of New York City, for use on the backs of all denominations of paper money is hereby approved, and you are instructed to proceed immediately with the engraving of a die of this design, completing the work at the earliest moment possible.

"I have caused this design to be prepared for use in connection with a change in the size of United States notes, gold and silver certificates and national-bank notes from their present dimensions to the dimensions of the Philippine certificates, and as soon as the engraving of the die of the new design is completed you will at once prepare plates for the printing of the classes above named of this reduced size.

"1. The engraving on the faces of the notes will be 2½ by 6⅛ inches and that on the backs will be 2¼ by 5⅞ inches."

This is the approved design by Cox referred to in MacVeagh's order to reduce U. S. currency size. It was to be used as the uniform back design for all denominations. Work had progressed to the point that George F. C. Smillie had engraved a die of the design which is shown in the above illustration.

With only minor revisions, this design was selected as the central feature for the back of the $100 Federal Reserve Note Series of 1914.

Mr. MacVeagh's instructions to the Bureau were given about a week before his retirement. He was succeeded in March, 1913 by Mr. McAdoo. Soon after the introduction of the new Secretary into office the chief of the Bureau of Engraving and Printing visited him and asked if the preparation of the new designs should be continued. Mr. McAdoo replied that he looked favorably on the proposal but instructed his Bureau chief to hold the matter up until he had time to go into it in detail. The setting up of the Federal Reserve system was then imminent and absorbed the attention of the Department for some time. Then the First World War commenced, and the order of Mr. MacVeagh was never executed.

Later Considerations and Recommendations

On June 6, 1922, President Harding wrote Secretary Mellon: "Personally I have long since been inclined to favor the smaller-sized bill. I had an opportunity of seeing some of the Philippine paper currency when it was first issued and thought it to be an ideal size. I wonder, however, if there would not be a curious psychological effect if we were to reduce the size of the currency at a time when there is a general complaint about the reduced purchasing power of our currency."

On September 10, 1923, Secretary Mellon announced a new series of designs. Instructions were given for the issue of these new designs and some of them were actually executed. Difficulties arose, however, which stopped the implementation of this program.

This redesign did not contemplate a change in size of notes. Secretary

Mellon, acting on the advice of the committee which prepared the designs, said in his annual report of 1923: "The proposition to reduce the size has been before the department for many years. Two reasons for the change have been advanced, (1) economy in production and handling, and (2) public convenience. The department is not aware of any public demand for the change, and it is doubtful if public convenience would be served. As regards economy in production and handling, there is no doubt the costs in these respects would be materially reduced. As a practical matter, however, it would be necessary to rebuild the entire mechanical equipment of the Bureau of Engraving and Printing now used for the production of paper currency, or else install new mechanical equipment; the cost in either case would be enormous. At the same time it would be necessary to continue the production of notes and certificates of existing designs until equipment could be made available to produce issues of the new designs, and consequently the difficulties of making the change with present facilities or with facilities which could be made available within a reasonable time, even if the necessary appropriation were available, would be almost insuperable. Aside from the practicability of the matter, however, it was felt that the size and general characteristics of the paper currency issues of the United States have been so firmly established and have given such universal satisfaction that no change should be made that might require the elimination of essential characteristics."

On November 12, 1924, Secretary Mellon appointed a new committee on currency design and instructed it to make an entirely new study of the subject.

On July 15, 1925, representatives of all the Federal Reserve Banks met in Washington to discuss currency matters and occasion was taken to place before them anew the proposal to reduce the size of currency notes. Reasons for and against the change were presented to the conference, concerning the following points:

1. Should the size be reduced.
2. If reduced, should the present width be retained and the length shortened.
3. If reduced, should both the length and width be reduced.

After discussion it was the unanimous opinion of the conference that the size should be reduced, that the reduction should apply to all kinds and denominations, and that the width as well as the length should be reduced.

The Federal Reserve Bank of San Francisco was not represented at the conference, but the Governor of that Bank wrote that "we have no proposals to offer further than my own opinion that it would be highly undesirable to reduce the size of one denomination (any denomination) and highly desirable to reduce the size of all denominations."

Origin of the Philippine Currency Size

On October 3, 1925, General McIntyre, of the Bureau of Insular Affairs, submitted memoranda to the Bureau of Efficiency throwing light on the origin and success of the Philippine size of paper currency. According to this data Dr. Meredith, of the Bureau of Engraving and Printing, had been asked to prepare designs for Philippine money. On April 24, 1903, he sent models of the face and back of the two-peso silver certificate. These models were found satisfactory but the Secretary of War, Elihu Root, was fearful that there might be confusion between the Philippine and American money. The possibility of using the smaller size was taken up with the Bureau, and the result was the initiation of the present size. It came about, it would seem, not because the size was regarded as better, but because it was different, and because it manufactured readily at the Bureau. In 1911, after eight years' use of this paper money, General Edwards, who had been chief of the Bureau of Insular Affairs all the time, wrote Senator Gallinger: "This paper has been satisfactory from every point of view and the size of the bills has been very favorably commented upon by a great many people." J. B. Peat, for many years a teller in the Philippine Treasury, appearing before the American Bankers' Association in 1910, said that he "was impressed with the suitability and serviceability of the banknote of the Philippine size. The smaller size note is a distinct advantage when compared with our own notes or with the still larger bank notes of the Spanish circulation. The smaller notes are not so subject to mutilation, nor are the corners so often turned up as in the case of the larger notes. In actual handling, counting and sorting the smaller size really facilitates the various operations. The initial cost of the smaller notes is considerably less, and they are more easily stored in vaults. For remitting purposes, either by post or express, the smaller notes will, of course, weigh considerably less. The adoption and circulation of notes of the Philippine size would be a material step toward improvement of American Currency."

A canvass of officers in the Bureau of Insular Affairs who had served in the Philippines showed that they were unanimously of the opinion, after handling the smaller-sized money, that it was more convenient than that used in the States. They said that, after years of service in the Philippines and use of this money, the currency at home seemed "like blankets" when they returned. They all believed that the Philippines had demonstrated, had definitely proved, the superiority of the smaller currency.

The Final Proposals of 1925

On August 20, 1925, the Treasury Department appointed a new General Currency Committee to restudy the whole question. This committee was broken up into eight subcommittees. Subcommittee No. 1 was instructed to study design. It was asked to report on:

1. New designs.
2. Uniform backs.
3. Denominational faces.
4. Use of color.
5. National bank notes.
6. Federal reserve notes.
7. Reduced size.

On October 17, 1925, this committee voted unanimously in favor of a proposal to recommend to the General Committee that the size of the paper currency of the United States be reduced to the size of that of the Philippines.

Summary

This search of the files of the Treasury Department disclosed the fact that through 15 years' discussion of the proposal to adopt the Philippine size for the paper currency of the United States, there was practical unanimity of opinion in favor of doing so. Mr. MacVeagh, Mr. Ralph, Mr. Broughton, Mr. Leffingwell, Mr. Gilbert, Mr. Houston, Mr. Kane, Mr. White, President Harding, the Federal Reserve Board, eleven out of the twelve of the heads of the Federal Reserve Banks (the twelfth merely failing to express an opinion), all gave their approval. Without exception these gentlemen believed that the change in size would result in economy and increased convenience to the public. Only the design committee of 1923 reported adversely. It did so because of its belief that adopting the smaller size would necessitate great changes at the Bureau of Engraving and Printing. Later investigations proved this not to be a fact.

ERROR AND FREAK NOTES

Though every effort is made to prevent error notes from slipping into circulation, some have occasionally been found by alert collectors. Error notes are those which show some irregularity from having gone incorrectly through one or more of the printing and cutting processes. Much collector interest has been focused on such notes, especially in recent years as a parallel to the spiraling demand for freak and error coins.

There are many ways an error can occur on currency. Consider that the sheets must undergo separate processes for printing the faces, backs, seal with serial numbers, overprint of signatures (and Bank seal) besides the trimming and cutting operations — and it is not hard to imagine all sorts of errors or error combinations appearing on some notes. The following illustrations will clearly show what can happen:

The above notes each have an extra flap of paper on one corner, the result of an accidental folding of their respective sheets before they were trimmed. The upper note has its flap turned out to show the face corner print with the back. The lower note has its flap folded down onto the face side to show that the back corner contains a portion of the overprinted seal and signature.

ERROR AND FREAK NOTES

This Federal Reserve Note never received any of the usual overprinting. Missing are Bank and Treasury seals, District numbers, series date, signatures and serial numbers.

The above note received its overprint, only the sheet was turned upside down as it was overprinted with seal, serial numbers, signatures and series date.

This note received only a partial overprint. Most of the seal and upper right serial number is missing.

ERROR AND FREAK NOTES

On rare occasions a piece of paper will adhere to a currency sheet, take some of the imprint, go through the various processes and fall off at a later time. The above note carries a large blank space formerly occupied by just such a piece of paper, perhaps a ream marker or some sort of tab. On rarer occasions, such a note *with the stray piece of paper still adhering to it* has been found.

When the finished sheets are stacked, the ink should of course be thoroughly dry. The above note shows the face design fully printed in retrograde on the back. The ink on the face side was still wet when the sheets were pressed together, and the dry back side simply picked up a backward surface impression of the face printing.

ERROR AND FREAK NOTES

This note has a long white streak of unprinted paper through the middle, the result of an inner fold in the sheet before the face side was printed.

This note has its serial numbers mis-matched, on the first digit.

This note carries a double impression because the sheet on which it was printed went twice through the same printing process.

ERROR AND FREAK NOTES

This note has the top of the next note showing, and a slice of its own top missing — the result of the sheet having moved either before trimming or before the notes were separated.

Aside from those illustrated, some other kinds of currency errors are as follows:

a. Double denomination notes, such as one showing $5 on the face and $10 on the back. This is the result of a sheet printed on one side being inadvertently placed with sheets of another denomination which were also printed only on one side. Such notes are among the rarest and most desirable of all errors.

b. Mis-matched type designation vs. overprint, such as a Silver Certificate frame with green seal, serial numbers and a Federal Reserve Bank seal. This is truly an amazing error, definitely known to exist but obviously of extreme rarity.

c. Inverted backs, the result of a sheet being turned upside down before receiving the printing for the backs of the notes.

d. Misplacement of overprint on the face — high, low, to the left or right.

e. Overprint for the face side printed on the back.

f. Uneven printing, where a section of the note may be lightly printed or practically missing.

On rare occasions a substantial quantity of notes may be made with a repeated mistake. A now-famous error occured during the printing of $1 Silver Certificates Series 1957, serial numbers in the G55------A issue. The second digit in the serial numbers was mis-matched (G55 vs. G54) on 10,000 of these dollars, which were stored until mid-1963 and then released at Ft. Benning, Georgia. The error was quickly noticed, resulting in widespread national publicity; many of them have since been absorbed in the numismatic market.

No standard of value can be applied to any error note. As a general rule, the severity of the mistake directly affects its numismatic desirability.

APPENDIX B

Official Bureau of Engraving Records
Showing Deliveries of Modern-Size Notes From 1929 to 1964

This section contains the records kept by the Bureau of Engraving for printings of modern U. S. currency. This material is helpful in determining the dates of issue of the various notes, and their grand totals.

As an aid to the use of this section, the Catalog number of each note or group of notes will be found in the left-hand column for easy correlation with the listing in the Catalog section.

Serial number data is also shown, purporting to contain the starting and ending serial numbers for any given series; unfortunately it is not accurate in this respect. It was the custom for some years to continue to use older plates until they were worn out, regardless of the fact that a newer series was being made and serially numbered at the same time. Thus, there is much overlap throughout the earlier series of modern-size notes. This same occurrence in later series is the result of changes in the logotype overprints which were not made simultaneously.

$1.00 UNITED STATES NOTES

No.	Serial Numbers	Inclusive Dates of Delivery	Total Delivered
12-Subject Sheets			
101-1	A00 000 001A A01 872 012A	Apr. 26, 1933 May 5, 1933	1,872,012

$2.00 UNITED STATES NOTES

No.	Serial Numbers	Inclusive Dates of Delivery	Total Delivered
12-Subject Sheets			
102-1 through **102-5**	A00 000 001A D29 712 000A	Apr. 24, 1929 Jan. 7, 1946	329,712,000*
102-6	D29 712 001A D36 192 000A	Feb. 25, 1946 Aug. 7, 1946	6,480,000
102-7	D36 192 001A D78 552 000A	Sept. 25, 1946 Dec. 6, 1949	42,360,000
102-8	D78 552 001A E30 760 000A	Jan. 16, 1950 May 6, 1953	52,208,000
18-Subject Sheets			
102-9	A00 000 001A A45 360 000A	May 2, 1953 Aug. 20, 1957	45,360,000
102-10	A45 360 001A A63 360 000A	Feb. 19, 1958 Sept. 8, 1960	18,000,000

*Further breakdown as to exact number made of each note is not available for Nos. 102-1 through 102-5.

$2.00 UNITED STATES NOTES

No.	Serial Numbers	Inclusive Dates of Delivery	Total Delivered
102-11	A63 360 001A A74 160 000A	Sept. 21, 1961 July 9, 1962	10,800,000
102-12	A74 160 001A A79 920 000A	Oct. 15, 1963 Nov. 7, 1963	5,760,000
	32-Subject Sheets		
102-13	A00 000 001A	Presently In Print	

$5.00 UNITED STATES NOTES

	12-Subject Sheets		
105-1 through **105-4**	A00 000 001A G50 628 000A	May 27, 1929 Feb. 25, 1946	650,628,000*
105-5	G50 628 001A G62 496 000A	Mar. 11, 1946 Sept. 19, 1946	11,868,000
105-6	G62 496 001A H71 592 000A	Sept. 20, 1946 Mar. 21, 1950	109,096,000
105-7	H71 592 001A I79 468 000A	Mar. 21, 1950 Apr. 27, 1953	107,876,000
	18-Subject Sheets		
105-8	A00 000 001A B20 880 000A	May 6, 1953 Aug. 28, 1957	120,880,000
105-9	B20 880 001A C11 160 000A	Feb. 10, 1958 Jan. 13, 1961	90,280,000
105-10	C11 160 001A C55 800 000A	Oct. 5, 1961 Feb. 25, 1963	44,640,000
105-11	C55 800 001A C64 440 000A	Feb. 26, 1963 Nov. 8, 1963	8,640,000
	32-Subject Sheets		
105-12	A00 000 001A	Presently In Print	

*Further breakdown as to exact number made of each note is not available for Nos. 105-1 through 105-4.

$1.00 SILVER CERTIFICATES

	12-Subject Sheets		
201-1 through **201-6**	A00 000 001A Z10 248 000B	Jan. 10, 1929 May 31, 1935	3,487,020,000*
201-7	A00 000 001A G82 176 000A	June 29, 1934 June 18, 1936	682,176,000
201-8	A00 000 001A R81 552 000A	Nov. 25, 1935 Sept. 9, 1938	1,681,552,000

*Further breakdown as to exact number made of each note is not available for Nos. 201-1 through 201-6.

$1.00 SILVER CERTIFICATES

No.	Serial Numbers	Inclusive Dates of Delivery	Total Delivered
201-9	R81 552 001A C93 384 000D	Sept. 9, 1938 July 27, 1945	6,111,832,000
201-10	C93 384 001D K99 996 000D	July 26, 1945 July 1, 1946	806,612,000
201-11	K99 996 001D R88 104 000E	June 25, 1946 July 11, 1949	3,088,108,000
201-12	R88 104 001E F99 999 999G	July 11, 1949 Aug. 5, 1952	
	H00 000 001G M98 128 000G	Aug. 5, 1952 Oct. 16, 1953	
	18-Subject Sheets		
	G00 000 001G G99 999 999G	Nov. 20, 1952 Jan. 14, 1953	
	N00 000 001G N46 944 000G	Jan. 14, 1953 Feb. 4, 1953	4,656,968,000
201-13	N46 944 001G P81 000 000I	Jan. 30, 1953 Dec. 31, 1957	5,134,056,000
201-15	P81 000 001I B54 000 000J	Dec. 31, 1957	
	B71 640 001J B72 000 000J	July 5, 1961	1,173,360,000
201-17	B54 000 001J B71 640 000J	June 9, 1961 July 5, 1961	
	B72 000 001J D48 960 000J	July 5, 1961 Mar. 12, 1962	194,600,000
201-18	D48 960 001J D80 280 000J	Apr. 2, 1962 Nov. 30, 1962	31,320,000
201-20	D80 280 001J E10 800 000J	June 10, 1963 Oct. 4, 1963	30,520,000
	32-Subject Sheets		
201-14	A00 000 001A B09 600 000B	Sept. 9, 1957 Mar. 3, 1961	2,609,600,000
201-16	A00 000 001A Q94 080 000A	Jan. 27, 1961 Feb. 7, 1963	1,594,080,000
201-19	Q94 080 001A Y12 480 000A	Jan. 17, 1963 Nov. 6, 1963	718,400,000

$5.00 SILVER CERTIFICATES

	12-Subject Sheets		
205-1	A00 000 001A D50 352 000A	July 20, 1934 Jan. 26, 1938	350,352,000

$5.00 SILVER CERTIFICATES

No.	Serial Numbers	Inclusive Dates of Delivery	Total Delivered
205-2	D50 352 001A	Jan. 27, 1938	
	K90 480 000A	Feb. 6, 1946	740,128,000
205-3	K90 480 001A	Feb. 6, 1946	
	L50 808 000A	Dec. 16, 1946	60,328,000
205-4	L50 808 001A	Dec. 19, 1946	
	Q23 136 000A	Oct. 24, 1949	372,328,000
205-5	Q23 136 001A	Oct. 25, 1949	
	V14 796 000A	Oct. 1, 1953	491,660,000

18-Subject Sheets

No.	Serial Numbers	Inclusive Dates of Delivery	Total Delivered
205-6	A00 000 001A	May 12, 1953	
	D39 600 000A	Aug. 21, 1957	339,600,000
205-7	D39 600 001A	Dec. 9, 1957	
	F72 000 000A	Mar. 17, 1961	232,400,000
205-8	F72 000 001A	Mar. 28, 1961	
	G45 000 000A	Apr. 25, 1962	73,000,000
205-9	G45 000 001A	Nov. 12, 1963	
	H35 640 000A	Aug. 31, 1964	90,640,000

$10.00 SILVER CERTIFICATES

12-Subject Sheets

No.	Serial Numbers	Inclusive Dates of Delivery	Total Delivered
210-1	A00 000 001A	Jan. 5, 1934	
	A00 216 000A	Feb. 27, 1934	216,000
210-1a	A00 216 001A	Feb. 27, 1934	
	A00 552 000A	Apr. 2, 1934	336,000
210-2	A00 552 001A	Apr. 17, 1934	
	A09 132 000A	Apr. 1, 1935	9,132,000
210-3	A09 132 001A	Apr. 2, 1935	
	B15 432 000A	Sept. 4, 1946	106,300,000
210-4	B15 432 001A	Sept. 4, 1946	
	B16 848 000A	Aug. 5, 1947	1,416,000
210-5	B16 848 001A	Aug. 5, 1947	
	B38 566 000A	July 12, 1950	21,718,000
210-6	B38 566 001A	July 12, 1950	
	B50 196 000A	Apr. 14, 1953	11,630,000

18-Subject Sheets

No.	Serial Numbers	Inclusive Dates of Delivery	Total Delivered
210-7	A00 000 001A	May 12, 1953	
	A10 440 000A	Aug. 27, 1957	10,440,000
210-8	A10 440 001A	Feb. 13, 1958	
	A11 520 000A	Feb. 17, 1958	1,080,000
210-9	A11 520 001A	Feb. 2, 1962	
	A12 240 000A	Mar. 14, 1962	720,000

Appendix B

$5.00 FEDERAL RESERVE BANK NOTES

No.	Serial Numbers	Inclusive Dates of Delivery	Total Delivered
		12-Subject Sheets	
405A	A00 000 001A	Mar. 11, 1933	
	A03 180 000A	Aug. 11, 1933	3,180,000
405B	B00 000 001A	Mar. 28, 1933	
	B02 100 000A	Aug. 19, 1933	2,100,000
405C	C00 000 001A	Mar. 11, 1933	
	C03 096 000A	Dec. 21, 1933	3,096,000
405D	D00 000 001A	Mar. 11, 1933	
	D04 236 000A	Nov. 22, 1933	4,236,000
405E	No Record	—	—
405F	F00 000 001A	Mar. 17, 1933	
	F01 884 000A	Mar. 30, 1933	1,884,000
405G	G00 000 001A	Mar. 16, 1933	
	G05 988 000A	Oct. 9, 1933	5,988,000
405H	H00 000 001A	Mar. 22, 1933	
	H00 276 000A	Mar. 30, 1933	276,000
405I	I00 000 001A	Mar. 23, 1933	
	I00 684 000A	Mar. 28, 1933	684,000
405J	J00 000 001A	Mar. 28, 1933	
	J02 460 000A	Jan. 11, 1934	2,460,000
405K	K00 000 001A	Mar. 18, 1933	
	K00 996 000A	Mar. 30, 1933	996,000
405L	L00 000 001A		
	L00 360 000A	Mar. 30, 1933	360,000

$10.00 FEDERAL RESERVE BANK NOTES

No.	Serial Numbers	Inclusive Dates of Delivery	Total Delivered
		12-Subject Sheets	
410A	A00 000 001A	Mar. 22, 1933	
	A01 680 000A	July 12, 1933	1,680,000
410B	B00 000 001A	Mar. 10, 1933	
	B05 556 000A	Oct. 14, 1933	5,556,000
410C	C00 000 001A	Mar. 28, 1933	
	C01 416 000A	Nov. 18, 1933	1,416,000
410D	D00 000 001A	Mar. 22, 1933	
	D02 412 000A	Nov. 4, 1933	2,412,000
410E	E00 000 001A	Mar. 17, 1933	
	E01 356 000A	Mar. 30, 1933	1,356,000
410F	F00 000 001A	Mar. 11, 1933	
	F01 056 000A	Mar. 31, 1933	1,056,000

$10.00 FEDERAL RESERVE BANK NOTES

No.	Serial Numbers	Inclusive Dates of Delivery	Total Delivered
410G	G00 000 001A	Mar. 13, 1933	
	G03 156 000A	Aug. 26, 1933	3,156,000
410H	H00 000 001A	Mar. 16, 1933	
	H01 584 000A	Mar. 30, 1933	1,584,000
410I	I00 000 001A	Mar. 22, 1933	
	I00 588 000A	Mar. 29, 1933	588,000
410J	J00 000 001A	Mar. 13, 1933	
	J01 284 000A	Mar. 30, 1933	1,284,000
410K	K00 000 001A	Mar. 29, 1933	
	K00 504 000A	Mar. 30, 1933	504,000
410L	L00 000 001A	Mar. 11, 1933	
	L01 080 000A	Mar. 30, 1933	1,080,000

$20.00 FEDERAL RESERVE BANK NOTES

12-Subject Sheets			
420A	A00 000 001A	Mar. 18, 1933	
	A00 972 000A	Mar. 29, 1933	972,000
420B	B00 000 001A	Mar. 14, 1933	
	B02 568 000A	Sept. 22, 1933	2,568,000
420C	C00 000 001A	Mar. 16, 1933	
	C01 008 000A	Mar. 29, 1933	1,008,000
420D	D00 000 001A	Mar. 21, 1933	
	D01 020 000A	Mar. 29, 1933	1,020,000
420E	E00 000 001A	Mar. 14, 1933	
	E01 632 000A	Mar. 27, 1933	1,632,000
420F	F00 000 001A	Apr. 18, 1933	
	F00 960 000A	Apr. 22, 1933	960,000
420G	G00 000 001A	Mar. 13, 1933	
	G02 028 000A	Sept. 28, 1933	2,028,000
420H	H00 000 001A	Mar. 13, 1933	
	H00 444 000A	Mar. 30, 1933	444,000
420I	I00 000 001A	Mar. 11, 1933	
	I00 864 000A	Mar. 21, 1933	864,000
420J	J00 000 001A	Mar. 30, 1933	
	J00 612 000A	Dec. 22, 1933	612,000
420K	K00 000 001A	Mar. 15, 1933	
	K00 468 000A	Mar. 16, 1933	468,000
420L	L00 000 001A	Mar. 20, 1933	
	L00 888 000A	Mar. 28, 1933	888,000

$50.00 FEDERAL RESERVE BANK NOTES

No.	Serial Numbers	Inclusive Dates of Delivery	Total Delivered
	12-Subject Sheets		
450A	No Record	———	———
450B	B00 000 001A B00 636 000A	Mar. 16, 1933 Mar. 29, 1933	636,000
450C	No Record	———	———
450D	D00 000 001A D00 684 000A	Mar. 17, 1933 Mar. 29, 1933	684,000
450E	No Record	———	———
450F	No Record	———	———
450G	G00 000 001A G00 300 000A	Aug. 29, 1933 Aug. 30, 1933	300,000
450H	No Record	———	———
450I	I00 000 001A I00 132 000A	Mar. 28, 1933 Mar. 29, 1933	132,000
450J	J00 000 001A J00 276 000A	Mar. 23, 1933 Mar. 30, 1933	276,000
450K	K00 000 001A K00 168 000A	Mar. 11, 1933 Mar. 17, 1933	168,000
450L	L00 000 001A L00 576 000A	Mar. 17, 1933 Mar. 25, 1933	576,000

$100 FEDERAL RESERVE BANK NOTES

No.	Serial Numbers	Inclusive Dates of Delivery	Total Delivered
	12-Subject Sheets		
400A	No Record	———	———
400B	B00 000 001A B00 480 000A	Mar. 20, 1933	480,000
400C	No Record	———	———
400D	D00 000 001A D00 276 000A	Mar. 16, 1933 Mar. 30, 1933	276,000
400E	E00 000 001A E00 192 000A	Mar. 11, 1933 Mar. 17, 1933	192,000
400F	No Record	———	———
400G	G00 000 001A G00 384 000A	Mar. 15, 1933 Mar. 29, 1933	384,000
400H	No Record	———	———
400I	I00 000 001A I00 144 000A	Mar. 23, 1933 Mar. 29, 1933	144,000
400J	J00 000 001A J00 096 000A	Mar. 24, 1933 Mar. 30, 1933	96,000
400K	K00 000 001A K00 036 000A	Mar. 20, 1933	36,000
400L	No Record	———	———

$1.00 FEDERAL RESERVE NOTES

32-Subject Sheets

No.	Starting Serial Numbers	First Date of Delivery	Total Delivered
501-1A	A00 000 001A	Nov. 19, 1963	Current
501-1B	B00 000 001A	Nov. 15, 1963	Current
501-1C	C00 000 001A	Nov. 15, 1963	Current
501-1D	D00 000 001A	Nov. 14, 1963	Current
501-1E	E00 000 001A	Nov. 18, 1963	Current
501-1F	F00 000 001A	Nov. 12, 1963	Current
501-1G	G00 000 001A	Nov. 7, 1963	Current
501-1H	H00 000 001A	Nov. 13, 1963	Current
501-1I	I00 000 001A	Nov. 18, 1963	Current
501-1J	J00 000 001A	Nov. 8, 1963	Current
501-1K	K00 000 001A	Nov. 6, 1963	Current
501-1L	L00 000 001A	Nov. 6, 1963	Current

$5.00 FEDERAL RESERVE NOTES

Combined Totals for
Series of 1928, 1928 A, 1928 B, 1928 C and 1928 D
Numbers 505-1A through 505-5F

12-Subject Sheets

Bank	Serial Numbers	Inclusive Dates of Delivery	Total Delivered
Boston	A00 000 001A A43 056 000A	Jan. 21, 1929 Jan. 10, 1934	43,056,000
New York	B00 000 001A B03 260 000B	Feb. 6, 1929 Oct. 13, 1934	103,260,000*
Philadelphia	C00 000 001A C46 560 000A	Feb. 7, 1929 Nov. 1, 1933	46,560,000
Cleveland	D00 000 001A D42 348 000A	Feb. 11, 1929 Jan. 11, 1934	42,348,000
Richmond	E00 000 001A E22 224 000A	Feb. 15, 1929 Oct. 13, 1932	22,224,000
Atlanta	F00 000 001A F30 024 000A	Feb. 16, 1929 May 28, 1935	30,024,000
Chicago	G00 000 001A G64 812 000A	Jan. 22, 1929 Dec. 1, 1934	64,812,000
St. Louis	H00 000 001A H28 008 000A	Feb. 25, 1929 Oct. 4, 1934	28,008,000
Minneapolis	I00 000 001A I11 436 000A	Feb. 27, 1929 Oct. 5, 1934	11,436,000

*See page 45 for clarification.

Appendix B

$5.00 FEDERAL RESERVE NOTES

Bank	Serial Numbers	Inclusive Dates of Delivery	Total Delivered
Kansas City	J00 000 001A J18 036 000A	Mar. 1, 1929 Oct. 7, 1933	18,036,000
Dallas	K00 000 001A K13 752 000A	Mar. 9, 1929 Aug. 13, 1935	13,752,000
San Francisco	L00 000 001A L43 728 000A	Jan. 30, 1929 Oct. 9, 1935	43,728,000

Combined Totals for Series of 1934 and 1934 A
Numbers 505-6AL through 505-7L
12-Subject Sheets

Boston	A00 000 001A A50 040 000A	Dec. 13, 1935 Jan. 4, 1946	50,040,000
New York	B00 000 001A B73 476 000B	Dec. 6, 1934 Nov. 16, 1945	173,476,000
Philadelphia	C00 000 001A C70 704 000A	Jan. 30, 1935 Nov. 23, 1945	70,704,000
Cleveland	D00 000 001A D57 660 000A	Dec. 13, 1935 Nov. 27, 1945	57,660,000
Richmond	E00 000 001A E66 060 000A	Dec. 13, 1935 Jan. 15, 1946	66,060,000
Atlanta	F00 000 001A F67 776 000A	June 7, 1935 Nov. 19, 1945	67,776,000
Chicago	G00 000 001A G11 736 000B	Jan. 23, 1935 Dec. 21, 1945	111,736,000
St. Louis	H00 000 001A H53 052 000A	Nov. 2, 1934 Mar. 6, 1946	53,052,000
Minneapolis	I00 000 001A I15 468 000A	Nov. 12, 1934 Sept. 11, 1944	15,468,000
Kansas City	J00 000 001A J30 984 000A	Dec. 13, 1935 Sept. 28, 1945	30,984,000
Dallas	K00 000 001A K31 560 000A	Aug. 12, 1935 Apr. 2, 1947	31,560,000
San Francisco	L00 000 001A L94 536 000A	Oct. 10, 1935 Mar. 7, 1946	94,536,000

Series of 1934 B
12-Subject Sheets

No.	Serial Numbers	Inclusive Dates of Delivery	Total Delivered
505-8A	A50 040 001A A54 588 000A	Jan. 5, 1946 Nov. 4, 1946	4,548,000
505-8B	B73 476 001B B94 548 000B	Nov. 19, 1945 Nov. 5, 1946	21,072,000
505-8C	C70 704 001A C80 424 000A	Dec. 4, 1945 Oct. 23, 1946	9,720,000

$5.00 FEDERAL RESERVE NOTES

No.	Serial Numbers	Inclusive Dates of Delivery	Total Delivered
505-8D	D57 660 001A D67 476 000A	Nov. 28, 1945 Jan. 16, 1947	9,816,000
505-8E	E66 060 001A E71 028 000A	Jan. 25, 1946 Nov. 14, 1946	4,968,000
505-8F	F67 776 001A F73 056 000A	Nov. 28, 1945 Dec. 31, 1946	5,280,000
505-8G	G11 736 001B G22 320 000B	Dec. 26, 1945 Nov. 4, 1946	10,584,000
505-8H	H53 052 001A H56 172 000A	Mar. 7, 1946 Sept. 17, 1946	3,120,000
505-8I	I15 468 001A I18 156 000A	May 2, 1946 Apr. 1, 1947	2,688,000
505-8J	J30 984 001A J31 728 000A	Feb. 11, 1947 Feb. 21, 1947	744,000
505-8K	None Printed		
505-8L	L94 536 001A L04 644 000B	Mar. 7, 1946 Nov. 19, 1946	10,108,000

Series of 1934 C

12-Subject Sheets

No.	Serial Numbers	Inclusive Dates of Delivery	Total Delivered
505-9A	A54 588 001A A68 376 000A	Nov. 5, 1946 Sept. 20, 1949	13,788,000
505-9B	B94 548 001B B57 780 000C	Nov. 5, 1946 Dec. 30, 1949	63,232,000
505-9C	C80 424 001A C02 268 000B	Nov. 6, 1946 Dec. 29, 1949	21,844,000
505-9D	D67 476 001A D87 888 000A	Jan. 20, 1947 Dec. 28, 1949	20,412,000
505-9E	E71 028 001A E93 996 000A	Nov. 27, 1946 Oct. 24, 1949	22,968,000
505-9F	F73 056 001A F94 776 000A	Mar. 12, 1947 Dec. 16, 1949	21,720,000
505-9G	G22 320 001B G80 064 000B	Nov. 4, 1946 Dec. 30, 1949	57,744,000
505-9H	H56 172 001A H75 996 000A	Sept. 30, 1946 Dec. 14, 1949	19,824,000
505-9I	I18 156 001A I22 980 000A	Apr. 17, 1947 Mar. 3, 1950	4,824,000
505-9J	J31 728 001A J38 112 000A	Feb. 27, 1947 May 1, 1950	6,384,000
505-9K	K31 560 001A K36 336 000A	Apr. 11, 1947 July 3, 1950	4,776,000
505-9L	L04 644 001B L12 492 000B	Nov. 19, 1946 Nov. 28, 1949	7,848,000

$5.00 FEDERAL RESERVE NOTES

Series of 1934 D

12-Subject Sheets

No.	Serial Numbers	Inclusive Dates of Delivery	Total Delivered
505-10A	A68 376 001A A80 554 000A	Jan. 10, 1950 Jan. 25, 1951	12,178,000
505-10B	B57 780 001C B12 704 000D	Jan. 3, 1950 Jan. 25, 1951	54,924,000
505-10C	C02 268 001B C15 064 000B	Jan. 16, 1950 Jan. 24, 1951	12,796,000
505-10D	D87 888 001A D98 308 000A	Jan. 5, 1950 Jan. 24, 1951	10,420,000
505-10E	E93 996 001A E07 170 000B	Jan. 10, 1950 Jan. 30, 1951	13,174,000
505-10F	F94 776 001A F04 812 000B	Jan. 6, 1950 Jan. 30, 1951	10,036,000
505-10G	G80 064 001B G16 640 000C	Jan. 12, 1950 Jan. 18, 1951	36,576,000
505-10H	H75 996 001A H83 792 000A	Feb. 1, 1950 Jan. 24, 1951	7,796,000
505-10I	I22 980 001A I26 628 000A	Mar. 13, 1950 Jan. 15, 1951	3,648,000
505-10J	J38 112 001A J44 924 000A	May 5, 1950 Jan. 25, 1951	6,812,000
505-10K	K36 336 001A K38 280 000A	July 12, 1950 Sept. 19, 1950	1,944,000
505-10L	L12 492 001B L23 776 000B	Feb. 1, 1950 Jan. 31, 1951	11,284,000

Series 1950

12-Subject Sheets

No.	Serial Numbers	Inclusive Dates of Delivery	Total Delivered
505-11A	A00 000 001A A30 672 000A	Feb. 7, 1951 July 28, 1953	30,672,000
505-11B	B00 000 001A B06 768 000B	Feb. 2, 1951 July 6, 1953	106,768,000
505-11C	C00 000 001A C44 784 000A	Feb. 28, 1951 June 23, 1953	44,784,000
505-11D	D00 000 001A D54 000 000A	Feb. 5, 1951 July 20, 1953	54,000,000
505-11E	E00 000 001A E47 088 000A	Nov. 7, 1950 July 14, 1953	47,088,000
505-11F	F00 000 001A F52 416 000A	Feb. 21, 1951 July 14, 1953	52,416,000

$5.00 FEDERAL RESERVE NOTES

No.	Serial Numbers	Inclusive Dates of Delivery	Total Delivered
505-11G	G00 000 001A G85 104 000A	Feb. 7, 1951 July 6, 1953	85,104,000
505-11H	H00 000 001A H36 864 000A	Feb. 21, 1951 July 6, 1953	36,864,000
505-11I	I00 000 001A I11 796 000A	Apr. 10, 1951 Sept. 1, 1953	11,796,000
505-11J	J00 000 001A J25 428 000A	Apr. 16, 1951 Sept. 1, 1953	25,428,000
505-11K	K00 000 001A K22 848 000A	Apr. 20, 1951 Aug. 28, 1953	22,848,000
505-11L	L00 000 001A L55 008 000A	Feb. 6, 1951 July 6, 1953	55,008,000

Serial numbers I11 796 001A — I11 808 000A, J25 428 001A — J25 488 000A, and K22 848 001A — K22 896 000A were respectively assigned for Minneapolis, Kansas City and Dallas notes but were never used.

Series 1950 A

18-Subject Sheets

No.	Serial Numbers	Inclusive Dates of Delivery	Total Delivered
505-12A	A30 672 001A A84 240 000A	July 31, 1953 Aug. 27, 1957	53,568,000
505-12B	B06 768 001B B93 240 000C	July 20, 1953 July 30, 1957	186,472,000
505-12C	C44 784 001A C14 400 000B	July 31, 1953 Aug. 27, 1957	69,616,000
505-12D	D54 000 001A D99 360 000A	July 30, 1953 Feb. 15, 1957	45,360,000
505-12E	E47 088 001A E23 760 000B	July 27, 1953 Aug. 12, 1957	76,672,000
505-12F	F52 416 001A F38 880 000B	July 16, 1953 Sept. 13, 1957	86,464,000
505-12G	G85 104 001A G14 400 000C	July 21, 1953 Aug. 7, 1957	129,296,000
505-12H	H36 864 001A H91 800 000A	July 6, 1953 Sept. 10, 1957	54,936,000
505-12I	I11 808 001A I23 040 000A	Sept. 25, 1953 July 16, 1956	11,232,000
505-12J	J25 488 001A J55 440 000A	Sept. 4, 1953 Aug. 10, 1956	29,952,000
505-12K	K22 896 001A K47 880 000A	Aug. 31, 1953 Aug. 29, 1957	24,984,000
505-12L	L55 008 001A L45 720 000B	July 14, 1953 July 8, 1957	90,712,000

Appendix B

$5.00 FEDERAL RESERVE NOTES

Series 1950 B

18-Subject Sheets

No.	Serial Numbers	Inclusive Dates of Delivery	Total Delivered
505-13A	A84 240 001A A15 120 000B	Sept. 25, 1957 May 29, 1961	30,880,000
505-13B	B93 240 001C B79 200 000D	Sept. 25, 1957 Sept. 30, 1960	85,960,000
505-13C	C14 400 001B C57 960 000B	Sept. 25, 1957 Mar. 23, 1961	43,560,000
505-13D	D99 360 001A D38 160 000B	Sept. 25, 1957 Jan. 31, 1961	38,800,000
505-13E	E23 760 001B E76 680 000B	Sept. 25, 1957 June 14, 1961	52,920,000
505-13F	F38 880 001B F19 440 000C	Sept. 25, 1957 Apr. 19, 1961	80,560,000
505-13G	G14 400 001C G18 720 000D	Sept. 25, 1957 Mar. 31, 1961	104,320,000
505-13H	H91 800 001A H17 640 000B	Sept. 25, 1957 Apr. 14, 1961	25,840,000
505-13I	I23 040 001A I43 920 000A	Sept. 25, 1957 Mar. 21, 1960	20,880,000
505-13J	J55 440 001A J87 840 000A	Sept. 25, 1957 Aug. 16, 1960	32,400,000
505-13K	K47 880 001A K99 999 999A	Sept. 25, 1957 May 12, 1961	52,119,999
505-13L	L45 720 001B L01 800 000C	Sept. 25, 1957 Mar. 28, 1961	56,080,000

Series 1950 C

18-Subject Sheets

505-14A	A15 120 001B A36 000 000B	Aug. 16, 1961 Feb. 1, 1963	20,880,000
505-14B	B79 200 001D B26 640 000E	Mar. 3, 1961 Dec. 17, 1962	47,440,000
505-14C	C57 960 001B C87 480 000B	Mar. 27, 1961 Nov. 7, 1962	29,520,000
505-14D	D38 160 001B D72 000 000B	May 4, 1961 Feb. 4, 1963	33,840,000
505-14E	E76 680 001B E10 080 000C	July 18, 1961 Mar. 1, 1963	33,480,000
505-14F	F19 440 001C F73 800 000C	May 12, 1961 Mar. 11, 1963	54,360,000
505-14G	G18 720 001D G75 600 000D	Apr. 3, 1961 Feb. 7, 1963	56,880,000

$5.00 FEDERAL RESERVE NOTES

No.	Serial Numbers	Inclusive Dates of Delivery	Total Delivered
505-14H	H17 640 001B H40 320 000B	July 18, 1961 Mar. 5, 1963	22,680,000
505-14I	I43 920 001A I56 880 000A	Aug. 16, 1961 Oct. 2, 1962	12,960,000
505-14J	J87 840 001A J12 600 000B	Aug. 18, 1961 Mar. 11, 1963	24,760,000
505-14K	K00 000 001B K03 960 000B	May 12, 1961 Jan. 2, 1963	3,960,000
505-14L	L01 800 001C L27 720 000C	July 28, 1961 Feb. 15, 1963	25,920,000

Series 1950 D

18-Subject Sheets

No.	Starting Serial Numbers	First Date of Delivery	Total Delivered
505-15A	A36 000 001B	Feb. 3, 1963	Current
505-15B	B26 640 001E	Dec. 19, 1962	Current
505-15C	C87 480 001B	Nov. 9, 1962	Current
505-15D	D72 000 001B	Feb. 6, 1963	Current
505-15E	E10 080 001C	Mar. 3, 1963	Current
505-15F	F73 800 001C	Mar. 13, 1963	Current
505-15G	G75 600 001D	Feb. 9, 1963	Current
505-15H	H40 320 001B	Mar. 7, 1963	Current
505-15I	I56 880 001A	Oct. 5, 1963	Current
505-15J	J12 600 001B	Mar. 14, 1963	Current
505-15K	K03 960 001B	Jan. 5, 1963	Current
505-15L	L27 720 001C	Feb. 17, 1963	Current

$10.00 FEDERAL RESERVE NOTES

Combined Totals for Series of 1928, 1928 A, 1928 B and 1928 C

Numbers 510-1A through 510-4G

12-Subject Sheets

Bank	Serial Numbers	Inclusive Dates of Delivery	Total Delivered
Boston	A00 000 001A A43 944 000A	Feb. 19, 1929 Oct. 6, 1934	43,944,000
New York	B00 000 001A B73 944 000A	Mar. 1, 1929 Aug. 16, 1934	73,944,000
Philadelphia	C00 000 001A C32 520 000A	Mar. 8, 1929 Nov. 1, 1934	32,520,000
Cleveland	D00 000 001A D32 532 000A	Mar. 22, 1929 Jan. 4, 1935	32,532,000

Appendix B

$10.00 FEDERAL RESERVE NOTES

Bank	Serial Numbers	Inclusive Dates of Delivery	Total Delivered
Richmond	E00 000 001A E17 604 000A	Mar. 28, 1929 Oct. 5, 1934	17,604,000
Atlanta	F00 000 001A F15 576 000A	Apr. 3, 1929 Aug. 19, 1935	15,576,000
Chicago	G00 000 001A G55 104 000A	Apr. 6, 1929 Oct. 22, 1934	55,104,000
St. Louis	H00 000 001A H15 360 000A	Apr. 8, 1929 Nov. 1, 1934	15,360,000
Minneapolis	I00 000 001A I09 120 000A	Apr. 13, 1929 Oct. 2, 1934	9,120,000
Kansas City	J00 000 001A J11 640 000A	Mar. 9, 1929 Dec. 5, 1934	11,640,000
Dallas	K00 000 001A K08 712 000A	Apr. 9, 1929 May 24, 1932	8,712,000
San Francisco	L00 000 001A L23 448 000A	Apr. 17, 1929 Sept. 19, 1935	23,448,000

Combined Totals for Series of 1934 and 1934 A

Numbers 510-5AL through 510-6L

12-Subject Sheets

Boston	A00 000 001A A38 292 000B	Nov. 9, 1934 Feb. 1, 1946	138,292,000
New York	B00 000 001A B71 688 000D*	Oct. 17, 1934 Nov. 21, 1945	371,688,000
Philadelphia	C00 000 001A C23 172 000B	Nov. 30, 1934 Feb. 19, 1946	123,172,000
Cleveland	D00 000 001A No Record	Feb. 16, 1935 No Record	No Record**
Richmond	E00 000 001A E10 992 000B	Jan. 23, 1935 Feb. 21, 1946	110,992,000
Atlanta	F00 000 001A F98 652 000A	Aug. 20, 1935 Jan. 30, 1946	98,652,000
Chicago	G00 000 001A G31 344 000C	Nov. 9, 1934 Dec. 5, 1945	231,344,000
St. Louis	H00 000 001A H69 528 000A	Nov. 30, 1934 Jan. 22, 1946	69,528,000
Minneapolis	I00 000 001A I31 392 000A	Dec. 10, 1934 Aug. 12, 1946	31,392,000
Kansas City	J00 000 001A J50 556 000A	Feb. 15, 1935 Feb. 6, 1946	50,556,000

*Higher serial numbers known (B80 865 669D).
**See notation on page 54 for explanation of this entry.

$10.00 FEDERAL RESERVE NOTES

Bank	Serial Numbers	Inclusive Dates of Delivery	Total Delivered
Dallas	K00 000 001A K44 688 000A	Dec. 13, 1935 Nov. 27, 1945	44,688,000
San Francisco	L00 000 001A L53 892 000B	Sept. 19, 1935 Feb. 15, 1946	153,892,000

Series of 1934 B

12-Subject Sheets

No.	Serial Numbers	Inclusive Dates of Delivery	Total Delivered
510-7A	A38 292 001B A44 772 000B	Feb. 8, 1946 Nov. 13, 1946	6,480,000
510-7B	B71 688 001D B14 304 000E	Nov. 23, 1945 Nov. 4, 1946	42,616,000
510-7C	C23 172 001B C33 504 000B	Feb. 19, 1946 Oct. 16, 1946	10,332,000
510-7D	No Record D17 328 000B	No Record Jan. 17, 1947	No Record*
510-7E	E10 992 001B E17 904 000B	Feb. 21, 1946 Dec. 4, 1946	6,912,000
510-7F	F98 652 001A F05 352 000B	Mar. 22, 1946 Dec. 19, 1946	6,700,000
510-7G	G31 344 001C G49 008 000C	Dec. 5, 1945 Oct. 30, 1946	17,664,000
510-7H	H69 528 001A H75 096 000A	Feb. 6, 1946 Oct. 10, 1946	5,568,000
510-7I	I31 392 001A I33 804 000A	Aug. 12, 1946 Apr. 2, 1947	2,412,000
510-7J	J50 556 001A J54 912 000A	Feb. 18, 1946 Jan. 3, 1947	4,356,000
510-7K	K44 688 001A K49 992 000A	Nov. 28, 1945 June 3, 1947	5,304,000
510-7L	L53 892 001B L63 132 000B	Feb. 15, 1946 Oct. 22, 1946	9,240,000

Series of 1934 C

12-Subject Sheets

No.	Serial Numbers	Inclusive Dates of Delivery	Total Delivered
510-8A	A44 772 001B A88 752 000B	Nov. 13, 1946 Nov. 1, 1949	43,980,000
510-8B	B14 304 001E B22 836 000F	Nov. 4, 1946 Sept. 28, 1949	108,532,000
510-8C	C33 504 001B C75 576 000B	Oct. 16, 1946 Oct. 14, 1949	42,072,000

*See page 54 for explanation.

Appendix B

$10.00 FEDERAL RESERVE NOTES

No.	Serial Numbers	Inclusive Dates of Delivery	Total Delivered
510-8D	D17 328 001B D60 480 000B	Jan. 17, 1947 Oct. 27, 1949	43,152,000
510-8E	E17 904 001B E52 356 000B	Dec. 4, 1946 Oct. 19, 1949	34,452,000
510-8F	F05 332 001B F49 704 000B	Dec. 11, 1946 Dec. 20, 1949	44,372,000
510-8G	G49 008 001C G46 464 000D	Oct. 30, 1946 Oct. 12, 1949	95,456,000
510-8H	H75 096 001A H08 616 000B	Oct. 24, 1946 Oct. 27, 1949	33,520,000
510-8I	I33 804 001A I43 740 000A	Apr. 14, 1947 Oct. 21, 1949	9,936,000
510-8J	J54 912 001A J74 748 000A	Jan. 9, 1947 Jan. 19, 1950	19,836,000
510-8K	K49 992 001A K73 032 000A	June 6, 1947 Dec. 20, 1949	23,040,000
510-8L	L63 132 001B L04 224 000C	Oct. 22, 1946 Oct. 3, 1949	41,092,000

Series of 1934 D

12-Subject Sheets

No.	Serial Numbers	Inclusive Dates of Delivery	Total Delivered
510-9A	A88 752 001B A08 724 000C	Nov. 1, 1949 Jan. 30, 1951	19,972,000
510-9B	B22 836 001F B83 288 000F	Sept. 28, 1949 Jan. 31, 1951	60,452,000
510-9C	C75 576 001B C94 760 000B	Oct. 14, 1949 Jan. 22, 1951	19,184,000
510-9D	D60 480 001B D80 700 000B	Oct. 27, 1949 Jan. 30, 1951	20,220,000
510-9E	E52 356 001B E71 000 000B	Oct. 19, 1949 Jan. 24, 1951	18,644,000
510-9F	F49 704 001B F66 884 000B	Dec. 20, 1949 Jan. 24, 1951	17,180,000
510-9G	G46 464 001D G02 156 000E	Oct. 13, 1949 Jan. 29, 1951	55,692,000
510-9H	H08 616 001B H22 412 000B	Oct. 27, 1949 Jan. 16, 1951	13,796,000
510-9I	I43 740 001A I49 132 000A	Nov. 7, 1949 Jan. 25, 1951	5,392,000
510-9J	J74 748 001A J82 740 000A	Mar. 14, 1950 Jan. 22, 1951	7,992,000
510-9K	K73 032 001A K80 712 000A	Feb. 9, 1950 Jan. 25, 1951	7,680,000
510-9L	L04 224 001C L28 536 000C	Oct. 17, 1949 Jan. 26, 1951	24,312,000

$10.00 FEDERAL RESERVE NOTES

Series 1950

12-Subject Sheets

No.	Serial Numbers	Inclusive Dates of Delivery	Total Delivered
510-10A	A00 000 001A A70 992 000A	July 14, 1951 May 20, 1953	70,992,000
510-10B	B00 000 001A B18 576 000C	Feb. 8, 1951 Apr. 1, 1953	218,576,000
510-10C	C00 000 001A C76 320 000A	Feb. 21, 1951 June 5, 1953	76,320,000
510-10D	D00 000 001A D76 032 000A	Feb. 7, 1951 May 6, 1953	76,032,000
510-10E	E00 000 001A E61 776 000A	Nov. 7, 1950 May 7, 1953	61,776,000
510-10F	F00 000 001A F63 792 000A	Feb. 20, 1951 June 12, 1953	63,792,000
510-10G	G00 000 001A G61 056 000B	Feb. 1, 1951 May 5, 1953	161,056,000
510-10H	H00 000 001A H47 808 000A	Mar. 19, 1951 June 5, 1953	47,808,000
510-10I	I00 000 001A I18 864 000A	Feb. 27, 1951 Oct. 1, 1953	18,864,000
510-10J	J00 000 001A J36 332 000A*	Feb. 28, 1951 Oct. 1, 1953	36,332,000
510-10K	K00 000 001A K33 264 000A	Feb. 27, 1951 Oct. 1, 1953	33,264,000
510-10L	L00 000 001A L76 896 000A	Feb. 6, 1951 May 13, 1953	76,896,000

*Serial numbers J36 332 001A — J36 432 000A were assigned for Kansas City notes but were never used.

Series 1950 A

18-Subject Sheets

No.	Serial Numbers	Inclusive Dates of Delivery	Total Delivered
510-11A	A70 992 001A A75 240 000B	May 27, 1953 Aug. 15, 1957	104,248,000
510-11B	B18 576 001C B75 240 000F	Apr. 3, 1953 Aug. 23, 1957	356,664,000
510-11C	C76 320 001A C48 240 000B	June 18, 1953 Apr. 30, 1957	73,920,000
510-11D	D76 032 001A D51 120 000B	May 22, 1953 Sept. 9, 1957	75,088,000
510-11E	E61 776 001A E43 920 000B	May 22, 1953 Aug. 21, 1957	82,144,000

Appendix B

$10.00 FEDERAL RESERVE NOTES

No.	Serial Numbers	Inclusive Dates of Delivery	Total Delivered
510-11F	F63 792 001A F37 080 000B	June 29, 1953 June 18, 1957	73,288,000
510-11G	G61 056 001B G96 120 000D	May 5, 1953 Sept. 12, 1957	235,064,000
510-11H	H47 808 001A H94 320 000A	June 29, 1953 Mar. 18, 1957	46,512,000
510-11I	I18 864 001A I27 000 000A	Oct. 1, 1953 June 30, 1955	8,136,000
510-11J	J36 432 001A J61 920 000A	Oct. 28, 1953 Aug. 7, 1956	25,488,000
510-11K	K33 264 001A K55 080 000A	Oct. 5, 1953 Sept. 3, 1957	21,816,000
510-11L	L76 896 001A L78 480 000B	May 15, 1953 May 15, 1957	101,584,000

Series 1950 B

18-Subject Sheets

No.	Serial Numbers	Inclusive Dates of Delivery	Total Delivered
510-12A	A75 240 001B A24 480 000C	Jan. 14, 1958 May 15, 1961	49,240,000
510-12B	B75 240 001F B46 080 000H	Sept. 25, 1957 Feb. 10, 1961	170,840,000
510-12C	C48 240 001B C15 120 000C	Dec. 12, 1958 Apr. 17, 1961	66,880,000
510-12D	D51 120 001B D06 480 000C	Sept. 25, 1957 Feb. 28, 1961	55,360,000
510-12E	E43 920 001B E95 040 000B	Dec. 18, 1957 May 4, 1961	51,120,000
510-12F	F37 080 001B F03 600 000C	Sept. 3, 1958 Apr. 5, 1961	66,520,000
510-12G	G96 120 001D G61 200 000F	Sept. 25, 1957 Apr. 4, 1961	165,080,000
510-12H	H94 320 001A H27 360 000B	Oct. 1, 1958 Apr. 19, 1961	33,040,000
510-12I	I27 000 001A I40 320 000A	July 23, 1958 Mar. 4, 1960	13,320,000
510-12J	J61 920 001A J95 400 000A	Oct. 1, 1957 Sept. 28, 1960	34,480,000
510-12K	K55 080 001A K81 360 000A	Sept. 25, 1957 Jan. 11, 1961	26,280,000
510-12L	L78 480 001B L33 480 000C	July 11, 1958 Jan. 10, 1961	55,000,000

$10.00 FEDERAL RESERVE NOTES

Series 1950 C

18-Subject Sheets

No.	Serial Numbers	Inclusive Dates of Delivery	Total Delivered
510-13A	A24 480 001C A75 600 000C	Sept. 1, 1961 Mar. 14, 1963	51,120,000
510-13B	B46 080 001H B66 600 000I	Mar. 2, 1961 Feb. 25, 1963	120,520,000
510-13C	C15 120 001C C40 320 000C	June 2, 1961 Nov. 20, 1962	25,200,000
510-13D	D06 480 001C D39 600 000C	July 27, 1961 Feb. 4, 1963	33,120,000
510-13E	E95 040 001B E40 680 000C	June 19, 1961 Mar. 14, 1963	45,640,000
510-13F	F03 600 001C F42 480 000C	May 26, 1961 Mar. 1, 1963	39,120,000
510-13G	G61 200 001F G30 600 001G	Apr. 5, 1961 Feb. 18, 1963	69,400,000
510-13H	H27 360 001B H50 400 000B	July 15, 1961 Mar. 11, 1963	23,040,000
510-13I	I40 320 001A I49 320 000A	Nov. 4, 1960 Oct. 3, 1962	9,000,000
510-13J	J95 400 001A J18 720 000B	Sept. 26, 1961 Mar. 8, 1963	23,320,000
510-13K	K81 360 001A K99 000 000A	Oct. 23, 1961 Jan. 2, 1963	17,640,000
510-13L	L33 480 001C L69 120 000C	Sept. 8, 1961 Feb. 19, 1963	35,640,000

Series 1950 D

18-Subject Sheets

No.	Starting Serial Numbers	First Date of Delivery	Total Delivered
510-14A	A75 600 001C	July 5, 1963	Current
510-14B	B66 600 001I	Feb. 25, 1963	Current
510-14C	C40 320 001C	Apr. 22, 1963	Current
510-14D	D39 600 001C	Feb. 20, 1963	Current
510-14E	E40 680 001C	Apr. 15, 1963	Current
510-14F	F42 480 001C	Apr. 8, 1963	Current
510-14G	G30 600 001G	Feb. 19, 1963	Current
510-14H	H50 400 001B	Aug. 22, 1963	Current
510-14I	I49 320 001A	No Record	Current
510-14J	J18 720 001B	Oct. 25, 1963	Current
510-14K	K99 000 001A	Nov. 1, 1963	Current
510-14L	L69 120 001C	Mar. 20, 1963	Current

$20.00 FEDERAL RESERVE NOTES

Combined Totals for Series of 1928, 1928 A, 1928 B and 1928 C

Numbers 520-1A through 520-4L

12-Subject Sheets

Bank	Serial Numbers	Inclusive Dates of Delivery	Total Delivered
Boston	A00 000 001A A12 168 000A	Apr. 5, 1929 Oct. 7, 1935	12,168,000
New York	B00 000 001A B31 500 000A	Apr. 9, 1929 Feb. 1, 1935	31,500,000
Philadelphia	C00 000 001A C13 440 000A	Apr. 16, 1929 Mar. 20, 1935	13,440,000
Cleveland	D00 000 001A D22 416 000A	Apr. 20, 1929 Sept. 18, 1935	22,416,000
Richmond	E00 000 001A E09 660 000A	Apr. 26, 1929 Oct. 27, 1934	9,660,000
Atlanta	F00 000 001A F07 416 000A	Apr. 27, 1929 Oct. 9, 1935	7,416,000
Chicago	G00 000 001A G31 020 000A	May 2, 1929 Mar. 23, 1935	31,020,000
St. Louis	H00 000 001A H06 852 000A	May 3, 1929 Oct. 31, 1934	6,852,000
Minneapolis	I00 000 001A I05 844 000A	May 6, 1929 May 1, 1935	5,844,000
Kansas City	J00 000 001A J07 440 000A	May 8, 1929 Aug. 15, 1935	7,440,000
Dallas	K00 000 001A K04 380 000A	May 13, 1929 Oct. 20, 1933	4,380,000
San Francisco	L00 000 001A L17 184 000A	May 9, 1929 Feb. 10, 1934	17,184,000

Combined Totals for Series of 1934 and 1934 A

Numbers 520-5A through 520-6L

12-Subject Sheets

Bank	Serial Numbers	Inclusive Dates of Delivery	Total Delivered
Boston	A00 000 001A A38 376 000A	Oct. 7, 1935 Sept. 27, 1945	38,376,000
New York	B00 000 001A B13 080 000B	Feb. 2, 1935 Nov. 29, 1945	113,080,000
Philadelphia	C00 000 001A C45 168 000A	Mar. 20, 1935 Dec. 26, 1945	45,168,000
Cleveland	D00 000 001A D67 164 000A	Sept. 19, 1935 Aug. 30, 1944	67,164,000

$20.00 FEDERAL RESERVE NOTES

Bank	Serial Numbers	Inclusive Dates of Delivery	Total Delivered
Richmond	E00 000 001A E72 036 000A	Feb. 2, 1935 Dec. 29, 1945	72,036,000
Atlanta	F00 000 001A F44 652 000A	Nov. 27, 1935 Nov. 28, 1945	44,652,000
Chicago	G00 000 001A G05 316 000B	Dec. 5, 1935 Feb. 4, 1946	105,316,000
St. Louis	H00 000 001A H29 364 000A	Feb. 7, 1935 Jan. 15, 1946	29,364,000
Minneapolis	I00 000 001A I16 296 000A	May 2, 1935 Sept. 29, 1944	16,296,000
Kansas City	J00 000 001A J28 812 000A	Aug. 16, 1935 Dec. 19, 1945	28,812,000
Dallas	K00 000 001A K22 164 000A	Dec. 27, 1935 Nov. 26, 1945	22,164,000
San Francisco	L00 000 001A L11 952 000B	Dec. 20, 1935 Dec. 11, 1945	111,952,000

Series of 1934 B

12-Subject Sheets

No.	Serial Numbers	Inclusive Dates of Delivery	Total Delivered
520-7A	A38 376 001A A41 832 000A	Apr. 15, 1946 Mar. 11, 1947	3,456,000
520-7B	B13 080 001B B37 980 000B	Nov. 29, 1945 Feb. 4, 1947	24,900,000
520-7C	C45 168 001A C50 568 000A	Feb. 18, 1946 Sept. 20, 1946	5,400,000
520-7D	D67 164 001A D71 124 000A	Feb. 1, 1946 Mar. 5, 1947	3,960,000
520-7E	E72 036 001A E81 030 000A	Feb. 8, 1946 Jan. 23, 1947	8,994,000
520-7F	F44 652 001A F53 628 000A	Nov. 29, 1945 Nov. 29, 1946	8,976,000
520-7G	G05 316 001B G15 036 000B	Feb. 4, 1946 Jan. 10, 1947	10,280,000
520-7H	H29 364 001A H35 184 000A	Apr. 8, 1946 Feb. 3, 1947	5,820,000
520-7I	I16 296 001A I19 332 000A	Dec. 14, 1945 Oct. 22, 1947	3,036,000
520-7J	J28 812 001A J33 000 000A	Feb. 14, 1946 Apr. 9, 1947	4,188,000
520-7K	K22 164 001A K25 044 000A	Feb. 27, 1946 Mar. 10, 1947	2,880,000
520-7L	L11 952 001B L21 672 000B	Dec. 11, 1945 Jan. 16, 1947	9,720,000

Appendix B

$20.00 FEDERAL RESERVE NOTES

Series of 1934 C

12-Subject Sheets

No.	Serial Numbers	Inclusive Dates of Delivery	Total Delivered
520-8A	A41 382 001A A49 584 000A	Mar. 12, 1947 Mar. 6, 1950	8,202,000
520-8B	B37 980 001B B55 860 000B	Feb. 4, 1947 Jan. 13, 1950	17,880,000
520-8C	C50 568 001A C62 556 000A	Jan. 7, 1947 Jan. 31, 1950	11,988,000
520-8D	D71 124 001A D88 380 000A	Mar. 19, 1947 Apr. 3, 1950	17,256,000
520-8E	E81 030 001A E04 668 000B	Jan. 23, 1947 Jan. 13, 1950	23,638,000
520-8F	F53 628 001A F72 084 000A	Apr. 14, 1947 Jan. 27, 1950	18,456,000
520-8G	G15 036 001B G40 752 000B	Jan. 10, 1947 Feb. 3, 1950	25,716,000
520-8H	H35 184 001A H48 864 000A	Jan. 18, 1947 Jan. 17, 1950	13,680,000
520-8I	I19 332 001A I22 614 000A	Nov. 3, 1947 Mar. 8, 1950	3,282,000
520-8J	J33 000 001A J41 880 000A	Sept. 26, 1947 Mar. 6, 1950	8,880,000
520-8K	K25 044 001A K34 992 000A	Mar. 20, 1947 July 3, 1950	9,948,000
520-8L	L21 672 001B L41 760 000B	Mar. 13, 1947 Feb. 16, 1950	20,088,000

Series of 1934 D

12-Subject Sheets

No.	Serial Numbers	Inclusive Dates of Delivery	Total Delivered
520-9A	A49 584 001A A53 936 000A	Mar. 10, 1950 Jan. 26, 1951	4,352,000
520-9B	B55 860 001B B71 320 000B	Jan. 13, 1950 Jan. 31, 1951	15,460,000
520-9C	C62 556 001A C66 444 000A	May 2, 1950 Jan. 2, 1951	3,888,000
520-9D	D88 380 001A D97 084 000A	May 1, 1950 Jan. 25, 1951	8,704,000
520-9E	E04 668 001B E18 480 000B	Jan. 13, 1950 Jan. 26, 1951	13,812,000
520-9F	F72 084 001A F79 576 000A	Jan. 31, 1950 Jan. 29, 1951	7,492,000

$20.00 FEDERAL RESERVE NOTES

No.	Serial Numbers	Inclusive Dates of Delivery	Total Delivered
520-9G	G40 752 001B G53 252 000B	Feb. 3, 1950 Jan. 29, 1951	12,500,000
520-9H	H48 864 001A H55 064 000A	Jan. 27, 1950 Jan. 26, 1951	6,200,000
520-9I	I22 614 001A I24 972 000A	Mar. 8, 1950 Jan. 15, 1951	2,358,000
520-9J	J41 880 001A J45 988 000A	Apr. 4, 1950 Jan. 25, 1951	4,108,000
520-9K	K34 992 001A K38 604 000A	July 11, 1950 Jan. 18, 1951	3,612,000
520-9L	L41 760 001B L55 176 000B	Feb. 17, 1950 Jan. 19, 1951	13,416,000

Series 1950

12-Subject Sheets

No.	Serial Numbers	Inclusive Dates of Delivery	Total Delivered
520-10A	A00 000 001A A23 184 000A	Feb. 16, 1951 Aug. 3, 1953	23,184,000
520-10B	B00 000 001A B80 064 000A	Feb. 7, 1951 Aug. 7, 1953	80,064,000
520-10C	C00 000 001A C29 520 000A	Mar. 5, 1951 July 23, 1953	29,520,000
520-10D	D00 000 001A D51 120 000A	Feb. 5, 1951 Aug. 3, 1953	51,120,000
520-10E	E00 000 001A E67 536 000A	Nov. 7, 1950 Aug. 3, 1953	67,536,000
520-10F	F00 000 001A F39 312 000A	Mar. 26, 1951 Aug. 14, 1953	39,312,000
520-10G	G00 000 001A G70 560 000A*	Feb. 1, 1951 Aug. 31, 1953	70,464,000
520-10H	H00 000 001A H27 360 000A*	Mar. 22, 1951 July 7, 1953	27,352,000
520-10I	I00 000 001A I09 216 000A	Apr. 11, 1951 Sept. 1, 1953	9,216,000
520-10J	J00 000 001A J22 752 000A	Mar. 6, 1951 Aug. 7, 1953	22,752,000
520-10K	K00 000 001A K22 752 000A*	Apr. 24, 1951 July 8, 1953	22,656,000
520-10L	L00 000 001A L70 272 000A	Feb. 6, 1951 Aug. 5, 1953	70,272,000

*Serial numbers G70 464 001A — G70 560 000A, H27 352 001A — H27 360 000A, and K22 656 001A — K22 752 000A were authorized for Chicago, St. Louis and Dallas notes, respectively, but were never used.

$20.00 FEDERAL RESERVE NOTES

Series 1950 A

18-Subject Sheets

No.	Serial Numbers	Inclusive Dates of Delivery	Total Delivered
520-11A	A23 184 001A A42 840 000A	Aug. 26, 1953 Aug. 27, 1957	19,656,000
520-11B	B80 064 001A B62 640 000B	Aug. 25, 1953 Aug. 30, 1957	82,568,000*
520-11C	C29 520 001A C46 080 000A	Aug. 26, 1953 June 6, 1955	16,560,000
520-11D	D51 120 001A D01 440 000B	Aug. 13, 1953 May 31, 1957	50,320,000
520-11E	E67 536 001A E37 080 000B	Aug. 19, 1953 Aug. 30, 1957	69,544,000
520-11F	F39 312 001A F66 960 000A	Aug. 24, 1953 Sept. 11, 1957	27,648,000
520-11G	G70 560 001A G44 280 000B	Aug. 31, 1953 Sept. 18, 1957	73,720,000
520-11H	H27 360 001A H50 040 000A	Aug. 28, 1953 Sept. 17, 1957	22,680,000
520-11I	I09 216 001A I14 760 000A	Sept. 29, 1953 June 27, 1955	5,544,000
520-11J	J22 752 001A J45 720 000A	Aug. 27, 1953 Aug. 6, 1956	22,968,000
520-11K	K22 752 001A K33 480 000A	Aug. 28, 1953 Aug. 1, 1957	10,728,000
520-11L	L70 272 001A L55 800 000B	Aug. 24, 1953 June 21, 1957	85,528,000

*B90 236 001A — B90 240 000A and B90 252 001A — B90 256 000A were not delivered. They were reported stolen, and when recovered they were destroyed. An account of this amazing robbery which took place at the Bureau in 1954 is included in the *History of the Bureau of Engraving and Printing,* pp 169-172.

Series 1950 B

18-Subject Sheets

No.	Serial Numbers	Inclusive Dates of Delivery	Total Delivered
520-12A	A42 840 001A A47 880 000A	July 10, 1958 Oct. 24, 1960	5,040,000
520-12B	B62 640 001B B12 600 000C	Oct. 11, 1957 Feb. 10, 1961	49,960,000
520-12C	C46 080 001A C54 000 000A	Nov. 24, 1958 Mar. 31, 1961	7,920,000
520-12D	D01 440 001B D39 600 000B	Sept. 25, 1957 Feb. 17, 1961	38,240,000
520-12E	E37 080 001B E79 200 000B	Jan. 20, 1958 June 16, 1961	42,120,000

$20.00 FEDERAL RESERVE NOTES

No.	Serial Numbers	Inclusive Dates of Delivery	Total Delivered
520-12F	F66 960 001A F07 200 000B	Sept. 2, 1958 Apr. 28, 1961	40,240,000
520-12G	G44 280 001B G24 840 000C	Sept. 25, 1957 Mar. 7, 1961	80,560,000
520-12H	H50 040 001A H69 480 000A	Sept. 25, 1957 Apr. 21, 1961	19,440,000
520-12I	I14 760 001A I27 000 000A	July 24, 1958 Mar. 14, 1960	12,240,000
520-12J	J45 720 001A J74 160 000A	Oct. 16, 1957 Sept. 13, 1960	28,440,000
520-12K	K33 480 001A K45 360 000A	Aug. 18, 1958 Jan. 24, 1961	11,880,000
520-12L	L55 800 001B L06 840 000C	July 1, 1958 Mar. 17, 1961	51,040,000

Series 1950 C

18-Subject Sheets

No.	Serial Numbers	Inclusive Dates of Delivery	Total Delivered
520-13A	A47 880 001A A55 080 000A	Sept. 20, 1961 Jan. 14, 1963	7,200,000
520-13B	B12 600 001C B55 800 000C	Feb. 28, 1961 Jan. 11, 1963	43,200,000
520-13C	C54 000 001A C61 560 000A	June 23, 1961 Sept. 13, 1962	7,560,000
520-13D	D39 600 001B D68 040 000B	May 25, 1961 Jan. 2, 1963	28,440,000
520-13E	E79 200 001B E16 200 000C	June 19, 1961 Mar. 21, 1963	37,000,000
520-13F	F07 200 001B F26 280 000B	May 1, 1961 Mar. 4, 1963	19,080,000
520-13G	G24 840 001C G54 000 000C	Apr. 3, 1961 Dec. 5, 1962	29,160,000
520-13H	H69 480 001A H82 440 000A	July 17, 1961 Mar. 19, 1963	12,960,000
520-13I	I27 000 001A I33 480 000A	Oct. 10, 1961 Sept. 7, 1962	6,480,000
520-13J	J74 160 001A J92 520 000A	Sept. 22, 1961 Mar. 19, 1963	18,360,000
520-13K	K45 360 001A K54 360 000A	July 10, 1961 Jan. 2, 1963	9,000,000
520-13L	L06 840 001C L52 200 000C	Sept. 6, 1961 Mar. 12, 1963	45,360,000

Appendix B

$20.00 FEDERAL RESERVE NOTES

Series 1950 D

18-Subject Sheets

No.	Starting Serial Numbers	First Date of Delivery	Total Delivered
520-14A	A55 080 001A	May 28, 1963	Current
520-14B	B55 800 001C	Feb. 25, 1963	Current
520-14C	C61 560 001A	Apr. 26, 1963	Current
520-14D	D68 040 001B	Feb. 12, 1963	Current
520-14E	E16 200 001C	Mar. 21, 1963	Current
520-14F	F26 280 001B	Apr. 19, 1963	Current
520-14G	G54 000 001C	Feb. 18, 1963	Current
520-14H	H82 440 001A	Aug. 30, 1963	Current
520-14I	I33 480 001A	No Record	Current
520-14J	J92 520 001A	Oct. 21, 1963	Current
520-14K	K54 360 001A	Nov. 29, 1963	Current
520-14L	L52 200 001C	Apr. 16, 1963	Current

$50.00 FEDERAL RESERVE NOTES

Combined Totals for Series of 1928 and 1928 A

Numbers 550-1A through 550-2L

12-Subject Sheets

Bank	Serial Numbers	Inclusive Dates of Delivery	Total Delivered
Boston	A00 000 001A A02 160 000A	June 13, 1929 Mar. 28, 1933	2,160,000
New York	B00 000 001A B04 548 000A	June 15, 1929 Dec. 10, 1934	4,548,000
Philadelphia	C00 000 001A C03 372 000A	June 14, 1929 Mar. 13, 1933	3,372,000
Cleveland	D00 000 001A D03 192 000A	June 14, 1929 July 21, 1933	3,192,000
Richmond	E00 000 001A E01 800 000A	June 19, 1929 Mar. 16, 1933	1,800,000
Atlanta	F00 000 001A F01 008 000A	June 18, 1929 Mar. 28, 1933	1,008,000
Chicago	G00 000 001A G06 360 000A	June 13, 1929 Mar. 11, 1933	6,360,000
St. Louis	H00 000 001A H01 092 000A	June 19, 1929 Mar. 18, 1933	1,092,000
Minneapolis	I00 000 001A I00 636 000A	June 19, 1929 Mar. 28, 1933	636,000

$50.00 FEDERAL RESERVE NOTES

Bank	Serial Numbers	Inclusive Dates of Delivery	Total Delivered
Kansas City	J00 000 001A J00 996 000A	June 19, 1929 Mar. 16, 1933	996,000
Dallas	K00 000 001A K00 756 000A	June 20, 1929 Mar. 28, 1933	756,000
San Francisco	L00 000 001A L01 512 000A	June 14, 1929 Mar. 12, 1933	1,512,000

Combined Totals for Series of 1934 and 1934 A
Numbers 550-3AL through 550-4L
12-Subject Sheets

Bank	Serial Numbers	Inclusive Dates	Total
Boston	A00 000 001A A02 940 000A	Dec. 18, 1935 July 19, 1944	2,940,000
New York	B00 000 001A B16 404 000A	Mar. 9, 1935 Jan. 2, 1949	16,404,000
Philadelphia	C00 000 001A C05 604 000A	Dec. 19, 1935 July 31, 1944	5,604,000
Cleveland	D00 000 001A D09 420 000A	Dec. 20, 1935 July 27, 1945	9,420,000
Richmond	E00 000 001A E06 648 000A	Dec. 19, 1935 July 31, 1945	6,648,000
Atlanta	F00 000 001A F03 276 000A	Dec. 18, 1935 July 13, 1946	3,276,000
Chicago	G00 000 001A G09 132 000A	Dec. 23, 1935 July 31, 1944	9,132,000
St. Louis	H00 000 001A H01 740 000A	Dec. 23, 1935 Nov. 16, 1945	1,740,000
Minneapolis	I00 000 001A I00 576 000A	Dec. 24, 1935 July 11, 1944	576,000
Kansas City	J00 000 001A J01 224 000A	Dec. 27, 1935 July 13, 1945	1,224,000
Dallas	K00 000 001A K01 392 000A	Dec. 26, 1935 July 17, 1945	1,392,000
San Francisco	L00 000 001A L07 824 000A	Dec. 26, 1935 Jan. 21, 1946	7,824,000

Series of 1934 B
12-Subject Sheets

No.	Serial Numbers	Inclusive Dates of Delivery	Total Delivered
550-5A	None Printed		
550-5B	None Printed		

Appendix B

$50.00 FEDERAL RESERVE NOTES

No.	Serial Numbers	Inclusive Dates of Delivery	Total Delivered
550-5C	C05 604 001A C05 880 000A	July 11, 1946 July 3, 1947	276,000
550-5D	D09 420 001A D09 444 000A	Aug. 19, 1947	24,000
550-5E	E06 648 001A E06 768 000A	July 12, 1946	120,000
550-5F	F03 276 001A F03 372 000A	July 23, 1946	96,000
550-5G	G09 132 001A G09 144 000A	July 11, 1949	12,000
550-5H	H01 740 001A H02 040 000A	Jan. 17, 1947 Jan. 20, 1947	300,000
550-5I	I00 576 001A I00 696 000A	July 28, 1947	120,000
550-5J	J01 224 001A J01 404 000A	July 24, 1946	180,000
550-5K	K01 392 001A K01 512 000A	July 29, 1947	120,000
550-5L	L07 824 001A L08 196 000A	July 25, 1946 Jan. 8, 1951	372,000

Series of 1934 C

12-Subject Sheets

No.	Serial Numbers	Inclusive Dates of Delivery	Total Delivered
550-6A	A02 940 001A A03 120 000A	Aug. 11, 1948 July 19, 1949	180,000
550-6B	B16 404 001A B18 072 000A	Jan. 2, 1949 July 20, 1950	1,668,000
550-6C	C05 880 001A C07 260 000A	Aug. 12, 1947 July 19, 1950	1,380,000
550-6D	D09 444 001A D12 184 000A	Aug. 19, 1947 Jan. 11, 1951	2,740,000
550-6E	E06 768 001A E09 048 000A	Aug. 19, 1947 July 19, 1950	2,280,000
550-6F	F03 372 001A F03 792 000A	Oct. 27, 1947 Oct. 28, 1947	420,000
550-6G	G09 144 001A G09 552 000A	July 11, 1949 July 20, 1950	408,000
550-6H	H02 040 001A H02 588 000A	Mar. 18, 1948 Jan. 9, 1951	548,000
550-6I	I00 696 001A I00 836 000A	Aug. 12, 1948 Jan. 8, 1951	140,000
550-6J	J01 404 001A J01 812 000A	Aug. 22, 1947 July 21, 1950	408,000

$50.00 FEDERAL RESERVE NOTES

No.	Serial Numbers	Inclusive Dates of Delivery	Total Delivered
550-6K	K01 512 001A K01 836 000A	Oct. 24, 1947 Feb. 1, 1950	324,000
550-6L	None Printed		

Series of 1934 D

12-Subject Sheets

No.	Serial Numbers	Inclusive Dates	Total Delivered
550-7A	A03 120 001A A03 468 000A	Aug. 18, 1950 Jan. 8, 1951	348,000
550-7B	B18 072 001A B19 248 000A	Sept. 28, 1950 Jan. 9, 1951	1,176,000
550-7C	C07 260 001A C08 004 000A	Dec. 4, 1950 Jan 12, 1951	744,000
550-7D	None Printed		
550-7E	E09 048 001A E09 216 000A	Jan. 9, 1951 Jan. 11, 1951	168,000
550-7F	F03 792 001A F04 020 000A	July 21, 1950 Jan. 11, 1951	228,000
550-7G	G09 552 001A G10 188 000A	Dec. 4, 1950 Jan. 11, 1951	636,000
550-7H	None Printed		
550-7I	None Printed		
550-7J	None Printed		
550-7K	K01 836 001A K01 984 000A	July 21, 1950 Jan. 9, 1951	148,000
550-7L	None Printed		

Series 1950

12-Subject Sheets

No.	Serial Numbers	Inclusive Dates	Total Delivered
550-8A	A00 000 001A A01 296 000A	Oct. 26, 1951 July 28, 1953	1,248,000
550-8B	B00 000 001A B10 368 000A	May 28, 1951 Aug. 28, 1953	10,236,000
550-8C	C00 000 001A C02 448 000A	May 9, 1951 July 28, 1953	2,352,000
550-8D	D00 000 001A D06 192 000A	July 13, 1951 July 23, 1953	6,180,000
550-8E	E00 000 001A E05 184 000A	Apr. 23, 1951 July 14, 1953	5,064,000
550-8F	F00 000 001A F01 872 000A	May 23, 1951 Feb. 6, 1953	1,812,000

$50.00 FEDERAL RESERVE NOTES

No.	Serial Numbers	Inclusive Dates of Delivery	Total Delivered
550-8G	G00 000 001A G04 320 000A	Nov. 26, 1951 July 17, 1953	4,212,000
550-8H	H00 000 001A H01 008 000A	Feb. 21, 1951 July 9, 1953	892,000
550-8I	I00 000 001A I00 432 000A	Nov. 5, 1951 July 23, 1953	384,000
550-8J	J00 000 001A J00 720 000A	May 21, 1951 July 21, 1953	696,000
550-8K	K00 000 001A K01 152 000A	Feb. 27, 1951 July 10, 1953	1,100,000
550-8L	L00 000 001A L04 032 000A	Apr. 23, 1951 July 31, 1953	3,996,000

The following serial numbers were not printed because of the changeover from 12-subject to 18-subject sheets:

A01 248 001A A01 296 000A	D06 180 001A D06 192 000A	G04 212 001A G04 320 000A
B10 236 001A B10 368 000A	E05 064 001A E05 184 000A	H00 892 001A H01 008 000A
C02 352 001A C02 448 000A	F01 812 001A F01 872 000A	

The following serial numbers were not printed:

K01 104 001A K01 152 000A	L03 996 001A L04 032 000A

The following serial numbers were transferred to the stock cage and delivered as mutilated October 30, 1953:

I00 384 001A I00 432 000A	J00 696 001A J00 720 000A	K01 100 001A K01 104 000A

Series 1950 A

18-Subject Sheets

No.	Serial Numbers	Inclusive Dates of Delivery	Total Delivered
550-9A	A01 296 001A A02 016 000A	Dec. 28, 1954 Aug. 12, 1957	720,000
550-9B	B10 368 001A B16 848 000A	Dec. 7, 1954 Jan. 23, 1957	6,480,000
550-9C	C02 448 001A C04 176 000A	Dec. 27, 1954 Aug. 20, 1957	1,728,000
550-9D	D06 192 001A D08 064 000A	Dec. 21, 1954 Jan. 16, 1957	1,872,000
550-9E	E05 184 001A E07 200 000A	Dec. 23, 1954 Aug. 15, 1957	2,016,000

$50.00 FEDERAL RESERVE NOTES

No.	Serial Numbers	Inclusive Dates of Delivery	Total Delivered
550-9F	F01 872 001A F02 160 000A	 Dec. 10, 1954	 288,000
550-9G	G04 320 001A G06 336 000A	Dec. 20, 1954 Jan. 23, 1957	 2,016,000
550-9H	H01 008 001A H01 584 000A	Dec. 13, 1954 Jan. 11, 1957	 576,000
550-9I	None Printed		
550-9J	J00 720 001A J00 864 000A	 Dec. 28, 1954	 144,000
550-9K	K01 152 001A K02 016 000A	Dec. 16, 1954 Oct. 14, 1955	 864,000
550-9L	L04 032 001A L04 608 000A	 Dec. 23, 1954	 576,000

Series 1950 B

18-Subject Sheets

No.	Serial Numbers	Inclusive Dates of Delivery	Total Delivered
550-10A	A02 016 001A A02 880 000A	Nov. 21, 1958 Sept. 1, 1960	 864,000
550-10B	B16 848 001A B25 200 000A	Nov. 5, 1957 Oct. 31, 1960	 8,352,000
550-10C	C04 176 001A C06 768 000A	Nov. 28, 1958 Nov. 29, 1960	 2,592,000
550-10D	D08 064 001A D09 792 000A	Oct. 13, 1958 Dec. 8, 1960	 1,728,000
550-10E	E07 200 001A E08 784 000A	July 28, 1958 Aug. 1, 1960	 1,584,000
550-10F	None Printed		
550-10G	G06 336 001A G10 656 000A	Sept. 30, 1957 Sept. 7, 1960	 4,320,000
550-10H	H01 584 001A H02 160 000A	Sept. 25, 1957 Sept. 25, 1959	 576,000
550-10I	None Printed		
550-10J	J00 864 001A J01 872 000A	Oct. 28, 1957 Aug. 9, 1960	 1,008,000
550-10K	K02 016 001A K03 024 000A	Nov. 21, 1958 Sept. 4, 1959	 1,008,000
550-10L	L04 608 001A L06 480 000A	Oct. 14, 1957 Aug. 8, 1960	 1,872,000

Appendix B

$50.00 FEDERAL RESERVE NOTES

Series 1950 C

18-Subject Sheets

No.	Serial Numbers	Inclusive Dates of Delivery	Total Delivered
550-11A	A02 880 001A A03 600 000A	Sept. 20, 1961 Sept. 11, 1962	720,000
550-11B	B25 200 001A B30 528 000A	Aug. 2, 1961 Dec. 4, 1962	5,328,000
550-11C	C06 768 001A C08 064 000A	July 31, 1961 Oct. 17, 1962	1,296,000
550-11D	D09 792 001A D11 088 000A	Oct. 18, 1961 Aug. 1, 1962	1,296,000
550-11E	E08 784 001A E10 080 000A	July 26, 1961 Nov. 14, 1962	1,296,000
550-11F	None Printed		
550-11G	G10 656 001A G12 384 000A	Sept. 21, 1961 Nov. 1, 1962	1,728,000
550-11H	H02 160 001A H02 736 000A	July 12, 1961 July 6, 1962	576,000
550-11I	I00 432 001A I00 576 000A	 Oct. 23, 1961	144,000
550-11J	J01 872 001A J02 304 000A	Oct. 26, 1961 Sept. 13, 1962	432,000
550-11K	K03 024 001A K03 744 000A	July 14, 1961 Dec. 3, 1962	720,000
550-11L	L06 480 001A L07 632 000A	Oct. 11, 1961 Oct. 31, 1962	1,152,000

Series 1950 D

18-Subject Sheets

No.	Starting Serial Numbers	First Date of Delivery	Total Delivered
550-12A	A03 600 001A	Aug. 30, 1963	Current
550-12B	B30 528 001A	Sept. 20, 1963	Current
550-12C	C08 064 001A	Oct. 29, 1963	Current
550-12D	D11 088 001A	Sept. 16, 1963	Current
550-12E	E10 080 001A	Aug. 30, 1963	Current
550-12F	F02 160 001A	Dec. 16, 1963	Current
550-12G	G12 384 001A	July 31, 1963	Current
550-12H	H02 736 001A	Sept. 24, 1963	Current
550-12I	I00 576 001A	July 26, 1963	Current
550-12J	J02 304 001A	Oct. 31, 1963	Current
550-12K	K03 744 001A	Nov. 7, 1963	Current
550-12L	L07 632 001A	July 19, 1963	Current

$100 FEDERAL RESERVE NOTES
Combined Totals for Series of 1928 and 1928 A
Numbers 500-1A through 500-2L
12-Subject Sheets

Bank	Serial Numbers	Inclusive Dates of Delivery	Total Delivered
Boston	A00 000 001A A01 320 000A	Aug. 30, 1929 Mar. 22, 1933	1,320,000
New York	B00 000 001A B03 528 000A	Sept. 21, 1929 Dec. 6, 1934	3,528,000
Philadelphia	C00 000 001A C01 704 000A	Aug. 30, 1929 Mar. 21, 1933	1,704,000
Cleveland	D00 000 001A D01 212 000A	Aug. 30, 1929 Mar. 6, 1933	1,212,000
Richmond	E00 000 001A E00 828 000A	Sept. 23, 1929 Mar. 23, 1933	828,000
Atlanta	F00 000 001A F00 612 000A	Sept. 23, 1929 Mar. 28, 1933	612,000
Chicago	G00 000 001A G04 140 000A	Aug. 30, 1929 Mar. 7, 1933	4,140,000
St. Louis	H00 000 001A H00 852 000A	Sept. 23, 1929 Mar. 28, 1933	852,000
Minneapolis	I00 000 001A I00 516 000A	Sept. 23, 1929 Mar. 28, 1933	516,000
Kansas City	J00 000 001A J00 780 000A	Sept. 23, 1929 Mar. 21, 1933	780,000
Dallas	K00 000 001A K00 420 000A	Nov. 25, 1929 Mar. 24, 1933	420,000
San Francisco	L00 000 001A L01 608 000A	Nov. 25, 1929 July 24, 1933	1,608,000

Combined Totals for Series of 1934 and 1934 A
Numbers 500-3AL through 500-4L
12-Subject Sheets

Boston	A00 000 001A A03 696 000A	Dec. 16, 1935 Jan. 12, 1951	3,696,000
New York	B00 000 001A B18 364 000A	Mar. 9, 1935 Jan. 19, 1951	18,364,000
Philadelphia	C00 000 001A C03 420 000A	Dec. 16, 1935 July 29, 1944	3,420,000
Cleveland	D00 000 001A D03 708 000A	Dec. 26, 1935 July 20, 1945	3,708,000
Richmond	E00 000 001A E04 332 000A	Dec. 30, 1935 Aug. 25, 1945	4,332,000
Atlanta	F00 000 001A F03 492 000A	Dec. 31, 1935 Aug. 25, 1945	3,492,000

Appendix B

$100 FEDERAL RESERVE NOTES

Bank	Serial Numbers	Inclusive Dates of Delivery	Total Delivered
Chicago	G00 000 001A G10 188 000A	Dec. 28, 1935 July 18, 1945	10,188,000
St. Louis	H00 000 001A H02 472 000A	Dec. 24, 1935 July 13, 1945	2,472,000
Minneapolis	I00 000 001A I00 900 000A	Dec. 26, 1935 July 24, 1945	900,000
Kansas City	J00 000 001A J02 268 000A	Dec. 28, 1935 July 16, 1945	2,268,000
Dallas	K00 000 001A K01 608 000A	Dec. 30, 1935 July 18, 1945	1,608,000
San Francisco	L00 000 001A L07 236 000A	Dec. 27, 1935 June 1, 1949	7,236,000

Series of 1934 B
12-Subject Sheets

No.	Serial Numbers	Inclusive Dates of Delivery	Total Delivered
500–5A	None Printed		
500–5B	None Printed		
500–5C	None Printed		
500–5D	D03 708 001A D03 720 000A	July 13, 1949	12,000
500–5E	E04 332 001A E04 572 000A	Nov. 13, 1946 Nov. 29, 1946	240,000
500–5F	F03 492 001A F03 612 000A	July 17, 1946	120,000
500–5G	G10 188 001A G10 200 000A	Aug. 4, 1947	12,000
500–5H	H02 472 001A H02 604 000A	July 17, 1946 Dec. 17, 1946	132,000
500–5I	I00 900 001A I01 020 000A	July 23, 1946	120,000
500–5J	J02 268 001A J02 280 000A	July 31, 1947	12,000
500–5K	K01 608 001A K01 648 000A	July 23, 1946	40,000
500–5L	None Printed		

Series of 1934 C
12-Subject Sheets

500–6A	None Printed
500–6B	None Printed
500–6C	None Printed

$100 FEDERAL RESERVE NOTES

No.	Serial Numbers	Inclusive Dates of Delivery	Total Delivered
500-6D	D03 720 001A D03 960 000A	July 13, 1949 Jan. 18, 1951	240,000
500-6E	E04 572 001A E06 844 000A	Aug. 4, 1947 Jan. 16, 1951	2,272,000
500-6F	F03 612 001A F04 572 000A	Aug. 6, 1947 July 15, 1949	960,000
500-6G	G10 200 001A G11 028 000A	Aug. 4, 1947 July 25, 1950	828,000
500-6H	H02 604 001A H03 852 000A	Dec. 31, 1946 Mar. 14, 1950	1,248,000
500-6I	I01 020 001A I01 652 000A	July 30, 1947 Jan. 17, 1951	632,000
500-6J	J02 280 001A J03 008 000A	July 31, 1947 Jan. 17, 1951	728,000
500-6K	K01 648 001A K02 328 000A	July 23, 1946 July 14, 1949	680,000
500-6L	L07 236 001A L07 808 000A	July 13, 1949 Jan. 15, 1951	572,000

Series of 1934 D

12-Subject Sheets

No.	Serial Numbers	Inclusive Dates of Delivery	Total Delivered
500-7A	None Printed		
500-7B	None Printed		
500-7C	C03 420 001A C03 780 000A	July 24, 1950 Jan. 17, 1951	360,000
500-7D	None Printed		
500-7E	None Printed		
500-7F	F04 572 001A F04 892 000A	July 25, 1950 Jan. 16, 1951	320,000
500-7G	G11 028 001A G11 368 000A	Jan. 15, 1951 Jan. 16, 1951	340,000
500-7H	H03 852 001A H04 236 000A	Jan. 16, 1951 Jan. 17, 1951	380,000
500-7I	None Printed		
500-7J	None Printed		
500-7K	K02 328 001A K02 480 000A	Aug. 17, 1950 Jan. 16, 1951	152,000
500-7L	None Printed		

$100 FEDERAL RESERVE NOTES

Series 1950

12-Subject Sheets

No.	Serial Numbers	Inclusive Dates of Delivery	Total Delivered
500-8A	A00 000 001A A00 768 000A	Nov. 7, 1952 July 27, 1953	768,000
500-8B	B00 000 001A B03 908 000A	Nov. 10, 1952 Sept. 9, 1953	3,908,000
500-8C	C00 000 001A C01 332 000A	May 9, 1951 July 31, 1953	1,332,000
500-8D	D00 000 001A D01 632 000A	Sept. 6, 1951 July 27, 1953	1,632,000
500-8E	E00 000 001A E04 076 000A	May 21, 1951 July 27, 1953	4,076,000
500-8F	F00 000 001A F01 824 000A	Sept. 4, 1951 July 16, 1953	1,824,000
500-8G	G00 000 001A G04 428 000A	Nov. 28, 1951 July 31, 1953	4,428,000
500-8H	H00 000 001A H01 284 000A	May 21, 1951 July 13, 1953	1,284,000
500-8I	I00 000 001A I00 564 000A	Feb. 8, 1952 July 23, 1953	564,000
500-8J	J00 000 001A J00 864 000A	Nov. 6, 1951 July 16, 1953	864,000
500-8K	K00 000 001A K01 216 000A	May 23, 1951 July 13, 1953	1,216,000
500-8L	L00 000 001A L02 524 000A	May 29, 1951 July 23, 1953	2,524,000

Series 1950 A

18-Subject Sheets

No.	Serial Numbers	Inclusive Dates of Delivery	Total Delivered
500-9A	A00 864 001A A01 872 000A	Dec. 28, 1954 Aug. 13, 1957	1,008,000
500-9B	B04 032 001A B06 912 000A	Dec. 13, 1954 Jan. 28, 1957	2,880,000
500-9C	C01 440 001A C02 016 000A	Dec. 10, 1954 Aug. 20, 1957	576,000
500-9D	D01 728 001A D02 016 000A	 Dec. 17, 1954	288,000
500-9E	E04 176 001A E06 336 000A	Dec. 20, 1954 Aug. 20, 1957	2,160,000
500-9F	F01 872 001A F02 160 000A	 Dec. 8, 1954	288,000
500-9G	G04 464 001A G05 328 000A	 Dec. 16, 1954	864,000

$100 FEDERAL RESERVE NOTES

No.	Serial Numbers	Inclusive Dates of Delivery	Total Delivered
500–9H	H01 296 001A H01 728 000A	Dec. 13, 1954 Jan. 4, 1957	432,000
500–9I	I00 576 001A I00 720 000A	Dec. 28, 1954	144,000
500–9J	J00 864 001A J01 152 000A	Dec. 28, 1954 Jan. 28, 1957	288,000
500–9K	K01 296 001A K01 728 000A	Dec. 15, 1954 Oct. 17, 1955	432,000
500–9L	L02 592 001A L03 312 000A	Dec. 14, 1954 Sept. 13, 1956	720,000

The following serial numbers were assigned but not printed:

A00 768 001A A00 864 000A	E04 076 001A E04 176 000A	I00 564 001A I00 576 000A
B03 908 001A B04 032 000A	F01 824 001A F01 872 000A	K01 216 001A K01 296 000A
C01 332 001A C01 440 000A	G04 428 001A G04 464 000A	L02 524 001A L02 592 000A
D01 632 001A D01 728 000A	H01 284 001A H01 296 000A	

Series 1950 B

18-Subject Sheets

No.	Serial Numbers	Inclusive Dates	Total
500–10A	A01 872 001A A02 592 000A	Nov. 18, 1958 Sept. 2, 1960	720,000
500–10B	B06 912 001A B13 248 000A	Dec. 18, 1957 Oct. 21, 1960	6,336,000
500–10C	C02 016 001A C02 736 000A	Oct. 6, 1959 Nov. 22, 1960	720,000
500–10D	D02 016 001A D02 448 000A	Sept. 25, 1957 Dec. 9, 1960	432,000
500–10E	E06 336 001A E07 344 000A	Sept. 3, 1959 Dec. 6, 1960	1,008,000
500–10F	F02 160 001A F02 736 000A	Aug. 4, 1959 Sept. 9, 1960	576,000
500–10G	G05 328 001A G07 920 000A	Sept. 25, 1957 Nov. 30, 1959	2,592,000
500–10H	H01 728 001A H02 880 000A	Oct. 1, 1957 Sept. 8, 1960	1,152,000
500–10I	I00 720 001A I01 008 000A	Nov. 17, 1959	288,000
500–10J	J01 152 001A J01 872 000A	Oct. 29, 1957 Aug. 10, 1960	720,000

$100 FEDERAL RESERVE NOTES

No.	Serial Numbers	Inclusive Dates of Delivery	Total Delivered
500-10K	K01 728 001A K03 456 000A	Sept. 4, 1957 Oct. 28, 1959	1,728,000
500-10L	L03 312 001A L06 192 000A	Oct. 15, 1957 Aug. 2, 1960	2,880,000

Series 1950 C

18-Subject Sheets

No.	Serial Numbers	Inclusive Dates of Delivery	Total Delivered
500-11A	A02 592 001A A03 456 000A	Sept. 12, 1961 Sept. 13, 1962	864,000
500-11B	B13 248 001A B15 696 000A	Sept. 28, 1961 Dec. 14, 1962	2,448,000
500-11C	C02 736 001A C03 312 000A	Aug. 28, 1961 Oct. 17, 1962	576,000
500-11D	D02 448 001A D03 024 000A	July 31, 1961 July 16, 1962	576,000
500-11E	E07 344 001A E08 784 000A	July 14, 1961 Nov. 1, 1962	1,440,000
500-11F	F02 736 001A F04 032 000A	Oct. 25, 1961 Oct. 5, 1962	1,296,000
500-11G	G07 920 001A G09 504 000A	Aug. 25, 1961 Nov. 1, 1962	1,584,000
500-11H	H02 880 001A H03 600 000A	July 12, 1961 Aug. 21, 1962	720,000
500-11I	I01 008 001A I01 296 000A	Oct. 20, 1961 Sept. 5, 1962	288,000
500-11J	J01 872 001A J02 304 000A	Sept. 20, 1961 Sept. 14, 1962	432,000
500-11K	K03 456 001A K04 176 000A	Jan. 10, 1962 Dec. 3, 1962	720,000
500-11L	L06 192 001A L08 352 000A	Nov. 29, 1961 Oct. 31, 1962	2,160,000

Series 1950 D

18-Subject Sheets

No.	Starting Serial Numbers	First Date of Delivery	Total Delivered
500-12A	A03 456 001A	Aug. 29, 1963	Current
500-12B	B15 696 001A	Aug. 16, 1963	Current
500-12C	C03 312 001A	Oct. 25, 1963	Current
500-12D	D03 024 001A	Sept. 13, 1963	Current
500-12E	E08 784 001A	July 31, 1963	Current
500-12F	F04 032 001A	Nov. 26, 1963	Current

$100 FEDERAL RESERVE NOTES

No.	Starting Serial Numbers	First Date of Delivery	Total Delivered
500-12G	G09 504 001A	Sept. 26, 1963	Current
500-12H	H03 600 001A	Sept. 10, 1963	Current
500-12I	I01 296 001A	No Record	Current
500-12J	J02 304 001A	Oct. 29, 1963	Current
500-12K	K04 176 001A	Nov. 29, 1963	Current
500-12L	L08 352 001A	July 23, 1963	Current

$500 FEDERAL RESERVE NOTES

Series of 1928

12-Subject Sheets

No.	Serial Numbers	Inclusive Dates of Delivery	Total Delivered
5500-1A	A00 000 001A A00 084 000A	Nov. 18, 1929 Mar. 12, 1933	84,000
5500-1B	B00 000 001A B00 340 800A	Nov. 8, 1929 Mar. 16, 1933	340,800
5500-1C	C00 000 001A C00 126 000A	Nov. 12, 1929 Mar. 16, 1933	126,000
5500-1D	D00 000 001A D00 154 320A	Nov. 12, 1929 Mar. 18, 1933	154,320
5500-1E	E00 000 001A E00 093 600A	Nov. 12, 1929 Mar. 18, 1933	93,600
5500-1F	F00 000 001A F00 064 200A	Nov. 13, 1929 Mar. 15, 1933	64,200
5500-1G	G00 000 001A G00 633 000A	Nov. 13, 1929 Mar. 15, 1933	633,000
5500-1H	H00 000 001A H00 092 400A	Nov. 13, 1929 Mar. 16, 1933	92,400
5500-1I	I00 000 001A I00 044 400A	Nov. 13, 1929 Mar. 15, 1933	44,400
5500-1J	J00 000 001A J00 091 800A	Nov. 14, 1929 Mar. 16, 1933	91,800
5500-1K	K00 000 001A K00 071 400A	Nov. 13, 1929 Mar. 18, 1933	71,400
5500-1L	L00 000 001A L00 105 000A	Nov. 14, 1929 Mar. 16, 1933	105,000

Series of 1934

12-Subject Sheets

No.	Serial Numbers	Inclusive Dates of Delivery	Total Delivered
5500-2A	A00 000 001A A00 058 200A	Dec. 23, 1935 July 25, 1940	58,200
5500-2B	B00 000 001A B00 526 800A	Dec. 26, 1935 July 31, 1944	526,800

$500 FEDERAL RESERVE NOTES

No.	Serial Numbers	Inclusive Dates of Delivery	Total Delivered
5500-2C	C00 000 001A C00 072 000A	Dec. 23, 1935 July 18, 1944	72,000
5500-2D	D00 000 001A D00 057 600A	Dec. 21, 1935 July 18, 1944	57,600
5500-2E	E00 000 001A E00 066 000A	Feb. 7, 1936 July 21, 1945	66,000
5500-2F	F00 000 001A F00 103 200A	Feb. 8, 1936 July 19, 1944	103,200
5500-2G	G00 000 001A G00 385 200A	Feb. 8, 1936 July 31, 1944	385,200
5500-2H	H00 000 001A H00 070 800A	Feb. 12, 1936 Aug. 1, 1944	70,800
5500-2I	I00 000 001A I00 025 200A	Feb. 12, 1936 July 18, 1944	25,200
5500-2J	J00 000 001A J00 079 200A	Feb. 13, 1936 July 21, 1945	79,200
5500-2K	K00 000 001A K00 054 000A	Feb. 13, 1936 July 21, 1945	54,000
5500-2L	L00 000 001A L00 158 400A	Feb. 13, 1936 July 21, 1945	158,400

Plates were engraved for Series of 1934 A, 1934 B and 1934 C, but no notes were printed from them.

$1,000 FEDERAL RESERVE NOTES

Series of 1928

12-Subject Sheets

No.	Serial Numbers	Inclusive Dates of Delivery	Total Delivered
5-1M-1A	A00 000 001A A00 052 800A	Nov. 14, 1929 Mar. 17, 1933	52,800
5-1M-1B	B00 000 001A B00 199 200A	Nov. 15, 1929 Mar. 17, 1933	199,200
5-1M-1C	C00 000 001A C00 091 200A	Nov. 15, 1929 Mar. 17, 1933	91,200
5-1M-1D	D00 000 001A D00 076 200A	Nov. 15, 1929 Mar. 14, 1933	76,200
5-1M-1E	E00 000 001A E00 055 200A	Nov. 16, 1929 Mar. 14, 1933	55,200
5-1M-1F	F00 000 001A F00 044 400A	Nov. 16, 1929 July 26, 1933	44,400
5-1M-1G	G00 000 001A G00 403 596A	Nov. 16, 1929 Mar. 11, 1933	403,596
5-1M-1H	H00 000 001A H00 055 200A	Nov. 16, 1929 Mar. 17, 1933	55,200
5-1M-1I	I00 000 001A I00 023 400A	Nov. 16, 1929 Mar. 13, 1933	23,400

$1,000 FEDERAL RESERVE NOTES

No.	Serial Numbers	Inclusive Dates of Delivery	Total Delivered
5-1M-1J	J00 000 001A J00 058 200A	Nov. 18, 1929 Mar. 17, 1933	58,200
5-1M-1K	K00 000 001A K00 036 600A	Nov. 18, 1929 Mar. 17, 1933	36,600
5-1M-1L	L00 000 001A L00 062 400A	Nov. 18, 1929 Mar. 17, 1933	62,400

Series of 1934

12-Subject Sheets

No.	Serial Numbers	Inclusive Dates of Delivery	Total Delivered
5-1M-2A	A00 000 001A A00 036 600A	Dec. 18, 1935 July 24, 1940	36,600
5-1M-2B	B00 000 001A B00 352 800A	Dec. 17, 1935 Dec. 27, 1942	352,800
5-1M-2C	C00 000 001A C00 036 000A	Dec. 20, 1935 July 27, 1942	36,000
5-1M-2D	D00 000 001A D00 027 000A	Dec. 21, 1935 Jan. 16, 1941	27,000
5-1M-2E	E00 000 001A E00 019 800A	Feb. 14, 1936 Nov. 17, 1943	19,800
5-1M-2F	F00 000 001A F00 044 400A	Jan. 31, 1935 June 19, 1942	44,400
5-1M-2G	G00 000 001A G00 116 400A	Feb. 15, 1936 June 14, 1940	116,400
5-1M-2H	H00 000 001A H00 022 800A	Feb. 14, 1936 July 29, 1943	22,800
5-1M-2I	I00 000 001A I00 007 200A	Feb. 14, 1936 July 27, 1942	7,200
5-1M-2J	J00 000 001A J00 027 600A	Feb. 15, 1936 July 20, 1943	27,600
5-1M-2K	K00 000 001A K00 036 600A	Feb. 14, 1936 Oct. 16, 1943	36,600
5-1M-2L	L00 000 001A L00 067 200A	Feb. 15, 1936 July 27, 1942	67,200

Series of 1934 A

12-Subject Sheets

No.	Serial Numbers	Inclusive Dates of Delivery	Total Delivered
5-1M-3A	A00 036 001A A00 059 000A	July 27, 1942 July 17, 1944	23,000
5-1M-3B	B00 352 801A B00 496 800A	Dec. 27, 1942 June 24, 1944	144,000

$1,000 FEDERAL RESERVE NOTES

No.	Serial Numbers	Inclusive Dates of Delivery	Total Delivered
5-1M-3C	C00 036 001A C00 096 000A	July 20, 1943 July 17, 1944	60,000
5-1M-3D	D00 027 001A D00 051 000A	July 21, 1943 July 17, 1944	24,000
5-1M-3E	E00 019 801A E00 028 800A	 Oct. 13, 1944	9,000
5-1M-3F	F00 044 401A F00 126 600A	July 20, 1943 July 21, 1945	82,200
5-1M-3G	G00 116 401A G00 279 600A	Mar. 30, 1942 July 18, 1944	163,200
5-1M-3H	H00 022 801A H00 054 000A	Feb. 3, 1944 Aug. 1, 1944	31,200
5-1M-3I	I00 007 201A I00 019 200A	 May 1, 1944	12,000
5-1M-3J	J00 027 601A J00 057 600A	Jan. 5, 1944 July 21, 1945	30,000
5-1M-3K	None Printed		
5-1M-3L	L00 067 201A L00 099 600A	Aug. 2, 1943 July 17, 1944	32,400

$5,000 FEDERAL RESERVE NOTES

Series of 1928

12-Subject Sheets

No.	Serial Numbers	Inclusive Dates of Delivery	Total Delivered
5-5M-1A	A00 000 001A A00 000 960A	Nov. 19, 1929 July 26, 1933	960
5-5M-1B	B00 000 001A B00 002 400A	 Jan. 20, 1929	2,400
5-5M-1C	None Printed		
5-5M-1D	D00 000 001A D00 002 400A	Nov. 19, 1929 Aug. 25, 1931	2,400
5-5M-1E	E00 000 001A E00 003 192A	Nov. 21, 1929 July 20, 1932	3,192
5-5M-1F	F00 000 001A F00 001 032A	Aug. 5, 1930 July 29, 1931	1,032
5-5M-1G	G00 000 001A G00 004 440A	Mar. 4, 1930 Mar. 8, 1933	4,440
5-5M-1H	None Printed		
5-5M-1I	None Printed		
5-5M-1J	J00 000 001A J00 000 480A	 Nov. 21, 1929	480
5-5M-1K	K00 000 001A K00 000 240A	 Mar. 4, 1930	240
5-5M-1L	L00 000 001A L00 001 224A	Nov. 19, 1929 July 23, 1930	1,224

$5,000 FEDERAL RESERVE NOTES

Series of 1934

12-Subject Sheets

No.	Serial Numbers	Inclusive Dates of Delivery	Total Delivered
5-5M-2A	A00 000 001A A00 006 000A	Dec. 19, 1935 July 26, 1940	6,000
5-5M-2B	B00 000 001A B00 007 800A	Dec. 19, 1935 May 7, 1940	7,800
5-5M-2C	C00 000 001A C00 000 600A	Dec. 19, 1935 July 26, 1940	600
5-5M-2D	D00 000 001A D00 001 200A	Dec. 19, 1936 No Record	1,200
5-5M-2E	E00 000 001A E00 001 200A	Feb. 17, 1936 No Record	1,200
5-5M-2F	F00 000 001A F00 001 200A	Feb. 17, 1936 No Record	1,200
5-5M-2G	G00 000 001A G00 004 800A	Feb. 17, 1936 Mar. 15, 1943	4,800
5-5M-2H	H00 000 001A H00 002 400A	Feb. 17, 1936 Oct. 18, 1943	2,400
5-5M-2I	None Printed		
5-5M-2J	J00 000 001A J00 001 200A	Feb. 17, 1936 No Record	1,200
5-5M-2K	K00 000 001A K00 001 200A	Feb. 17, 1936 No Record	1,200
5-5M-2L	L00 000 001A L00 003 000A	Feb. 17, 1936 Jan. 16, 1941	3,000

$10,000 FEDERAL RESERVE NOTES

Series of 1928

12-Subject Sheets

5-10M-1A	A00 000 001A A00 000 960A	Nov. 22, 1929 July 26, 1933	960
5-10M-1B	B00 000 001A B00 002 400A	Jan. 18, 1930 Dec. 6, 1933	2,400
5-10M-1C	None Printed		
5-10M-1D	D00 000 001A D00 000 600A	Apr. 7, 1930	600

$10,000 FEDERAL RESERVE NOTES

No.	Serial Numbers	Inclusive Dates of Delivery	Total Delivered
5-10M-1E	E00 000 001A E00 001 992A	Nov. 22, 1929 Mar. 8, 1933	1,992
5 10M 1F	F00 000 001A F00 001 032A	Aug. 5, 1930 July 29, 1932	1,032
5-10M-1G	G00 000 001A G00 002 400A	Mar. 8, 1933	2,400
5-10M-1H	None Printed		
5-10M-1I	None Printed		
5-10M-1J	J00 000 001A J00 000 240A	Nov. 22, 1929	240
5-10M-1K	K00 000 001A K00 000 240A	Mar. 4, 1930	240
5-10M-1L	L00 000 001A L00 001 224A	Nov. 22, 1929 July 23, 1930	1,224

Series of 1934

12-Subject Sheets

No.	Serial Numbers	Inclusive Dates of Delivery	Total Delivered
5-10M-2A	A00 000 001A A00 003 600A	Dec. 18, 1935 July 25, 1940	3,600
5-10M-2B	B00 000 001A B00 007 800A	Dec. 18, 1935 Apr. 23, 1940	7,800
5-10M-2C	C00 000 001A C00 000 600A	July 26, 1940	600
5-10M-2D	None Printed		
5-10M-2E	None Printed		
5-10M-2F	None Printed		
5-10M-2G	G00 000 001A G00 003 600A	Feb. 18, 1936 July 8, 1944	3,600
5-10M-2H	H00 000 001A H00 001 200A	Feb. 18, 1936 Oct. 18, 1943	1,200
5-10M-2I	None Printed		
5-10M-2J	None Printed		
5-10M-2K	None Printed		
5-10M-2L	L00 000 001A L00 001 800A	Feb. 18, 1936 Jan. 16, 1941	1,800

GOLD CERTIFICATES

All printed in sheets of 12 subjects.

$10.00 Gold Certificates

No.	Serial Numbers	Inclusive Dates of Delivery	Total Delivered
610-1	A00 000 001A B30 812 000A	May 29, 1929 Feb. 6, 1933	130,812,000
610-2	B30 812 001A B33 356 000A	Mar. 28, 1933 Apr. 14, 1933	2,544,000

$20.00 Gold Certificates

| **620-1** | A00 000 001A A66 204 000A | May 29, 1929 Feb. 8, 1933 | 66,204,000 |
| **620-2** | A66 204 001A A67 704 000A | Apr. 18, 1933 Apr. 28, 1933 | 1,500,000 |

$50.00 Gold Certificates

| **650** | A00 000 001A A05 520 000A | Aug. 21, 1929 Oct. 26, 1931 | 5,520,000 |

$100 Gold Certificates

| **600** | A00 000 001A A03 240 000A | Oct. 1, 1929 Oct. 24, 1931 | 3,240,000 |
| Series of 1934 | A00 000 001A A00 120 000A | June 25, 1934 | 120,000 |

$500 Gold Certificates

| **6500** | A00 000 001A A00 420 000A | Dec. 2, 1929 Oct. 20, 1930 | 420,000 |

$1,000 Gold Certificates

| **6-1M** | A00 000 001A A00 288 000A | Dec. 2, 1929 Oct. 20, 1930 | 288,000 |
| Series of 1934 | A00 000 001A A00 084 000A | June 25, 1934 | 84,000 |

$5,000 Gold Certificates

| **6-5M** | A00 000 001A A00 024 000A | Nov. 29, 1929 Dec. 10, 1929 | 24,000 |

$10,000 Gold Certificates

No.	Serial Numbers	Inclusive Dates of Delivery	Total Delivered
6–10M	A00 000 001A A00 048 000A	Nov. 23, 1929	48,000
Series of 1934	A00 000 001A A00 036 000A	June 25, 1934	36,000

$100,000 Gold Certificates

Series of 1934	A00 000 001A A00 042 000A	Jan. 9, 1935	42,000

WORLD WAR II ISSUES

Yellow Seal North Africa Silver Certificates

One Dollar

A201	B30 000 001C B31 000 000C	First lot delivered Sept. 4, 1942.	26,916,000
	B51 624 001C B52 624 000C		
	B99 000 001C B99 999 999C	Last lot delivered April 24, 1944.	

C60 000 001C C62 000 000C		C78 000 001C C79 904 000C

F41 952 001C ⎫ This lot was delivered to the
F41 955 996C ⎭ Treasurer in uncut sheets.

F41 955 977C F41 964 000C	I30 000 001C I40 000 000C	R90 000 001C R99 999 999C

Five Dollars

A205–1 and A205–2	K34 188 001A K34 508 000A	First lot delivered Sept. 4, 1942.	16,660,000
	K36 420 001A K36 740 000A		
	K37 464 001A K37 784 000A	Last lot delivered May 8, 1944.	

K40 068 001A K42 068 000A	K43 152 001A K44 852 000A	K53 984 001A K65 984 000A

Ten Dollars

No.	Serial Numbers	Inclusive Dates of Delivery	Total Delivered
A210-1 and A210-2	A91 044 001A A92 764 000A	First lot delivered Sept. 4, 1942.	21,860,000
	A92 764 001A A99 999 999A		
	B00 000 001A B00 904 000A	Last lot delivered May 8, 1944.	
	B01 564 001A B13 564 000A		

Experimental "R" and "S" $1.00 Silver Certificates

No.	Serial Numbers	Date of Delivery	Total Delivered
R201	S70 884 001C S72 068 000C	June 20, 1944	1,184,000
S201	S73 884 001C S75 068 000C	June 20, 1944	1,184,000

$1.00 HAWAII Silver Certificates

No.	Serial Numbers		Total Delivered
H201	Y68 628 001B Y71 628 000B	First lot delivered June 8, 1942.	35,052,000
	Z99 000 001B Z99 999 999B		
	A99 000 001C A99 999 999C	Last lot delivered June 8, 1944.	
	C00 000 001C C07 000 000C		
	F41 964 001C ⎫ This lot was delivered to the F41 967 996C ⎭ Treasurer in uncut sheets.		
	F41 967 997C F41 976 000C	L75 996 001C L78 996 000C	
	P31 992 001C P37 032 000C	S39 996 001C S54 996 000C	

Appendix B

$5.00 HAWAII S.F. Federal Reserve Notes

No.	Serial Numbers	Inclusive Dates of Delivery	Total Delivered
H505-1	L12 396 001A L14 996 000A	First lot delivered June 8, 1942.	3,000,000
	L19 776 001A L20 176 000A		
H505-2	L46 404 001A L47 804 000A		6,416,000
	L54 072 001A L56 088 000A		
	L66 132 001A L69 132 000A	Last lot delivered May 30, 1944.	

$10.00 HAWAII S.F. Federal Reserve Notes

H-510	L65 856 001A L66 456 000A	First lot delivered June 8, 1942.	10,424,000
	L67 476 001A L69 076 000A		
	L69 736 001A L71 336 000A		
	L77 052 001A L77 172 000A	Last lot delivered July 12, 1944.	
	L11 160 001B L12 664 000B		

L28 212 001B	L43 032 001B	L50 292 001B
L29 712 000B	L45 532 000B	L51 292 000B

$20.00 HAWAII S.F. Federal Reserve Notes

H520-1 **and** **H520-2**	L30 540 001A L31 090 000A	First lot delivered June 8, 1942.	11,246,000
	L31 632 001A L32 032 000A		
	L33 420 001A L34 220 000A	Last lot delivered July 18, 1944.	
	L56 412 001A L56 912 000A		

L60 588 001A	L67 984 001A	L76 980 001A	L85 536 001A
L61 592 000A	L69 976 000A	L78 480 000A	L90 036 000A

THE NEW U. S. PAPER CURRENCY WILL BE THIS SIZE

According to latest information the new bills will bear a portrait of a famous American on the front:

Washington	. .	$ 1
Jefferson	. .	$ 2
Lincoln	. .	$ 5
Hamilton	. .	$10
Jackson	. .	$20
Grant	. .	$50

The $1 bills and denominations over $100 will have ornamental backs. All the others will have engravings of buildings on the backs.

Franklin	. .	$ 100
McKinley	.	$ 500
Cleveland	.	$ 1,000
Madison	. .	$ 5,000
Chase	. . .	$10,000

It is estimated that the reduced size of the new paper currency will save the government several million dollars in printing cost.

IT WILL NOT BE IN CIRCULATION UNTIL JULY 1, 1929

This is an example of a privately made circular describing the coming "reduced size" currency Such circulars were distributed by various businessmen shortly before the new currency was placed into circulation in 1929 The back of the one shown contains an advertisement.

—————•◆•—————

BIBLIOGRAPHY

Along with various smaller articles from a wide variety of sources, the following books and periodicals were consulted:

Donlon, William P., *Donlon Price Catalog of United States Small Size Paper Money,* Hewitt Bros., Chicago, Illinois, First Edition, 1964

Friedberg, Robert, *Paper Money of the United States,* Coin and Currency Institute, Inc., New York, 5th Edition, 1964

History of the Bureau of Engraving and Printing 1862-1962, Treasury Department, Washington, D.C., 1964

Lloyd, Robert H., *National Bank Notes, Federal Reserve Bank Notes, Federal Reserve Notes 1928-1950,* Coin Collector's Journal, January-February 1953, Wayte Raymond, Inc., 1953

Lloyd, Robert H., *Check List of Silver Certificates,* Coin Collector's Journal, June, 1936—also other articles that appeared in various issues of this magazine

The Numismatist

Numismatic Scrapbook Magazine

COINS Magazine

Paper Money, published by the Society of Paper Money Collectors

Tom's Currency Album

INDEX

INDEX

INDEX